Verbal Reasoning

The 11+ 10-Minute Tests

For the CEM (Durham University) test

Ages **10-11**

Practise • Prepare • Pass

Everything your child needs for 11+ success

How to use this book

This book is made up of 10-minute tests and puzzle pages.
There are answers and detailed explanations in the pull-out section at the back of the book.

10-Minute Tests

- There are 32 tests in this book, each containing either 20 or 26 questions.

- Each test is designed to cover a good range of the question styles and topics that your child could see in the verbal reasoning section of their 11+ test, at the same difficulty level.

- Your child should aim to score around 17 out of 20 or 22 out of 26 in each of the 10-minute tests. If they score less than this, use their results to work out the areas they need more practice on.

- If your child hasn't managed to finish the test in time, they need to work on increasing their speed, whereas if they have made a lot of mistakes, they need to work more carefully.

- Keep track of your child's scores using the progress chart on the inside back cover of the book.

Puzzle Pages

- There are 6 puzzle pages in this book. The puzzles are a great break from test preparation. They also encourage children to practise the same skills that they will need in the test, but in a fun way.

Published by CGP

Editors:
Joanna Daniels, Ben Ffrancon Davies, Heather McClelland, Sabrina Robinson

With thanks to Holly Poynton and Maxine Petrie for the proofreading.

ISBN: 978 1 78294 261 0
Printed by Elanders Ltd, Newcastle upon Tyne
Clipart from Corel®

Based on the classic CGP style created by Richard Parsons.

Contents

Test 1

You have **10 minutes** to do this test. Work as quickly and accurately as you can.

Read this passage carefully and answer the questions that follow.

The Eiffel Tower

The Eiffel Tower characterises the Paris skyline, and it is one of the world's most famous monuments, drawing over 7 million visitors annually.

The Eiffel Tower was designed as an entry for the World's Fair — a celebration held in Paris between May and October back in 1889. Before it was built, several
5 French artists believed that building a structure the size of the Eiffel Tower, especially out of metal, would be an abhorrent departure from Paris's existing architecture, which included buildings such as the Notre Dame Cathedral and the Arc de Triomphe.

However, the engineer in charge of the project, Gustave Eiffel, was confident that
10 people would come to admire his project. Upon its completion in 1889, the Eiffel Tower was the tallest man-made structure in the world, standing at 300 metres. It held this title until the Chrysler Building skyscraper in New York was completed in 1930. A broadcast aerial was added to the Eiffel Tower in 1957, making it 20 metres taller than its original height.

15 The tower opened to the public on the 6th May, and, as Eiffel had predicted, the exhibition was a hit. Over 28 million visitors passed under the legs of this giant during the World Fair, with 1,896,987 of them ascending the tower itself. Since then, over 250 million people have admired the view of Paris from the tower's balconies — ascending either by the lifts or by climbing its 1,665 steps.

20 The Eiffel Tower had permission to stay in place for twenty years. However, Paris officials decided that the tower served as an effective communications tower, especially for sending wireless telegraph signals. In 1910, the tower was granted a reprieve, and since then has become an iconic feature of both Paris and France.

Answer these questions about the text that you've just read.
Circle the letter that matches the correct answer.

1. Why were some people not in favour of the Eiffel Tower?

   A Because it would obstruct people's view of the Paris skyline.

   B Because fewer people would visit the existing monuments.

   C Because it would steal the show at the World's Fair.

   D Because it wouldn't be in keeping with Paris's other buildings.

2. According to the text, what's the most significant difference between the Eiffel Tower and the Arc de Triomphe?

   A It is made of metal.

   B It is very tall.

   C It isn't a cathedral.

   D It is a tourist attraction.

3. How tall was the Eiffel Tower in 1960?

   A 276 metres

   B 300 metres

   C 320 metres

   D 350 metres

4. Which of the following is not mentioned in the text?

   A What increased the height of the Eiffel Tower in 1957

   B What the World's Fair was

   C Who designed the Chrysler Building

   D What the Eiffel Tower is made out of

5. Which of the following statements about the Eiffel Tower is not true?

A The artists' protest against it being built was unsuccessful.

B There are over 1,500 steps to the top.

C It was over half a kilometre in height when it was finished.

D Gustave Eiffel's prediction about its success was correct.

6. When was the Eiffel Tower supposed to be taken down?

A 1989

B 1909

C 1910

D 1930

7. Why was the Eiffel Tower initially allowed to remain standing?

A It had become an emblem of France and Paris.

B It was useful for sending communication signals.

C It proved very popular with tourists.

D It was considered too beautiful to take down.

In each question below, the words can be rearranged to form a sentence. One word doesn't fit in the sentence. Underline the word that doesn't fit.

Example: red the has <u>ride</u> girl bicycle a

8. yesterday lawn have the mow tomorrow will to I

9. exciting rugby many sport great think an people is

10. cancelled is been it because school rained has snowing

11. took but drinks too of was tea she a hot sip it

12. latest is best instalment books this yet one the

13. was young the too film funnier for children far scary

14. brightly darkness his shone among through torch the

Find the word that means the opposite, or nearly the opposite, of the word on the left.

Example: **first** later last next beginning

15. **celebrate** deject commiserate detest regret

16. **chastise** punish vindicate embellish commend

17. **inconsequential** sequential unimportant paramount tolerable

18. **demonic** intimidating angelic monstrous provocative

19. **minute** gargantuan second discernible obvious

20. **irrelevant** rational pertinent dependable retrievable

END OF TEST

/20

Test 2

You have **10 minutes** to do this test. Work as quickly and accurately as you can.

Fill in the missing letters to complete the words in the following passage.

1. Wolfgang Amadeus Mozart — more c _ m _ _ n _ y known by just
2. his s _ r _ a _ e — was a musician, who was born over 250 years ago in what is now Austria.
3. His love a f _ _ _ r with music started at a very young age, and he
4. quickly p _ o _ _ d himself to be a skilled violinist and pianist.
5. He composed a huge amount of music, writing over 600 p _ _ c _ s including symphonies and operas. Many of these works are still played today.
6. Writing so much at a time when music was a c r _ _ _ a l part of
7. society, he left a prestigious l e _ a _ _ behind him. He has
8. i n _ _ _ e n _ e d many musicians, from contemporaries like
9. Beethoven to modern musical s _ _ o _ a r s.
10. Despite being an r _ n _ w _ e _ musician, his work did not offer
11. him much f i n _ _ _ _ a l security, and he died almost
12. d e s _ _ t _ _ e.

Complete the word on the right so that it means the opposite, or nearly the opposite, of the word on the left.

Example: heavy [l] [i] [g] [h] [t]

13. extinguish [ ] [ ] [n] [ ] [t] [e]

14. dishevel [ ] [r] [ ] [ ] [m]

15. tire [e] [ ] [ ] [r] [ ] [ ] [z] [e]

16. careless [ ] [a] [u] [t] [ ] [ ] [ ] [s]

17. bravery [c] [o] [ ] [ ] [r] [ ] [ ] [c] [e]

Three of the words in each list are linked. Mark the word that is not related to these three.

Example: journal diary <u>textbook</u> notebook

18. lack scarcity famine shortage

19. victorious fulfilment accomplishment success

20. happy sympathetic content delighted

21. beautiful stunning striking gracious

22. gift balloon party card

In each question below, the words can be rearranged to form a sentence. One word doesn't fit in the sentence. Underline the word that doesn't fit.

Example: red the has <u>ride</u> girl bicycle a

m 23. clocks has wall a picture the frame nice on that

m 24. stars sky of twinkle whole up thousands lit the

M 25. swung bang knock loud the open door a with

m 26. enough there concert is to plenty for time of practise the

END OF TEST

/ 26

Test 3

10

You have **10 minutes** to do this test. Work as quickly and accurately as you can.

Read this passage carefully and answer the questions that follow.

An Extract from 'What Katy Did at School'

"Oh! What is it? What has happened?" cried Clover, starting up in bed the next morning, as a clanging sound roused her suddenly from sleep. It was only the rising-bell, ringing at the end of Quaker Row.

Katy held her watch up to the dim light. She could just see the hands. Yes: they
5 pointed to six. It was actually morning! She and Clover jumped up, and began to dress as fast as possible.

"We've only got half an hour," said Clover, unhooking the rules, and carrying them to the window, — "Half an hour; and this says that we must turn the mattress, smooth the under-sheet over the bolster, and spend five minutes in silent devotion!
10 We'll have to be quick to do all that besides dressing ourselves!"

It is never easy to be quick, when one is in a hurry. Everything sets itself against you. Fingers turn into thumbs; dresses won't button, nor pins keep their place. With all their haste, Katy and Clover were barely ready when the second bell sounded. As they hastened downstairs, Katy fastening her breast-pin, and Clover her cuffs, they
15 met other girls, some looking half asleep, some half dressed; all yawning, rubbing their eyes, and complaining of the early hour.

"Isn't it horrid?" said Lilly Page, hurrying by with no collar on, and her hair hastily tucked into a net. "I never get up till nine o'clock when I'm at home. Ma saves my breakfast for me. She says I shall have my sleep out while I have the chance."

Susan Coolidge

Answer these questions about the text that you've just read.
Circle the letter that matches the correct answer.

1. Why does Clover cry out and start up in bed?

   A She is startled by the morning bell.

   B She has had a bad dream.

   C Katy has woken her up.

   D Something bad has happened.

2. By what time do the girls have to be ready?

   A 5:30 am

   B 6:00 am

   C 6:30 am

   D 6:35 am

3. How do you know that Clover hasn't been at the school very long?

   A She finds it difficult to get up so early.

   B She doesn't know where the light switch is.

   C She is agitated.

   D She is surprised by how much there is to do in the morning.

4. What does the author mean by "Fingers turn into thumbs" (line 12)?

   A They are panicking.

   B Thumbs are completely useless.

   C Rushing makes them clumsy.

   D The buttons on their clothes won't fasten properly.

5. What information in the text tells you that religion is important at the school?

A The girls have to get up very early.

B The girls have a strict morning routine.

C The school is just for girls.

D The girls have to pray before lessons.

6. What do the girls all have in common?

A They all like their new school.

B They don't usually get up until nine o'clock.

C None of them are used to getting up this early.

D None of them are dressed properly.

7. Why does Lilly Page's mother let her sleep in?

A If she woke up earlier, her breakfast wouldn't be ready.

B She knows that she'll have to get up early at school.

C There's no need for her to wake up any earlier.

D She thinks it's unhealthy to get up too early.

In each question below, the words can be rearranged to form a sentence. One word doesn't fit in the sentence. Underline the word that doesn't fit.

Example: red the has <u>ride</u> girl bicycle a

8. herself could reflection she mirror her see the own in

9. cannot watch the I wait next episode for

10. drive car would start to the walk not we had so

11. the steam the pie there rising an table was from on

12. open summer will the day pool in swim be all

13. packed always entirety tourists of centre the is city full

Complete the word on the right so that it means the same, or nearly the same, as the word on the left.

Example: scared a f r a i d

14. rest r e _ a _

15. stroll a _ _ l e

16. disintegrate _ r _ _ _ l e

17. relish _ a v _ _ r

18. prevent _ _ _ d e r

19. reasonable _ _ n s _ _ l e

20. constant _ o n t _ _ a l

END OF TEST

/ 20

Test 4

You have **10 minutes** to do this test. Work as quickly and accurately as you can.

Choose the correct words to complete the passage below.

If you play a musical instrument, you should

1. ☐ think
 ☐ pondering
 ☐ consider
 ☐ aim

joining an orchestra.

Playing in an orchestra can be an excellent way to

2. ☐ practise
 ☐ practising
 ☐ practice
 ☐ practised

your musical talents and meet new friends.

3. ☐ Neither
 ☐ Weather
 ☐ Nor
 ☐ Whether

you have a violin, a flute or even an

4. ☐ xylophone
 ☐ oboe
 ☐ clarinet
 ☐ harp

— almost any instrument is welcome!

With a

5. ☐ some
 ☐ plenty
 ☐ loads
 ☐ bit

of hard work, you could find yourself playing songs from your favourite films and musicals.

6. ☐ Who
 ☐ When
 ☐ Why
 ☐ What

you've spent a lot of time learning a difficult piece, it can be very satisfying to

7. ☐ perform
 ☐ represent
 ☐ display
 ☐ playing

it to a hall full of people, especially if

they 8. ☐ enjoy ☐ enjoyed ☐ enjoying ☐ enjoys listening to it just as 9. ☐ lots ☐ similarly ☐ equally ☐ much as you like playing it.

Some of the best school orchestras get the chance to 10. ☐ travels ☐ tour ☐ visits ☐ journeys the world,

showcasing the talent that they have to offer. It 11. ☐ need ☐ require ☐ demanding ☐ takes hard work to become

a good musician, but it's one of the most 12. ☐ bad ☐ exciting ☐ greatest ☐ good hobbies in the world.

Complete the word on the right so that it means the same, or nearly the same, as the word on the left.

Example: scared a f r a i d

13. grin s _ _ _ e

M 14. collect _ o m _ i _ e

M 15. eject e _ _ _ l

16. wander s _ _ _ _ e r

Mark the word outside the brackets that has a similar meaning to the words in both sets of brackets.

Example: (twig branch) (fasten attach) glue <u>stick</u> affix bough

17. (role character) (separate divide) play split cast part

18. (hut outhouse) (remove discard) shed strip moult annex

19. (hang dangle) (adjourn postpone) delay suspend drape droop

20. (clue hint) (notice banner) signal indication sign detect

21. (photo drawing) (imagine visualize) cartoon picture dream sight

Three of the words in each list are linked. Mark the word that is not related to these three.

Example: journal diary <u>textbook</u> notebook

22. dialogue lecture conversation discussion

23. glass mug china plastic

24. trade exchange swap goods

25. break burst shatter smash

26. book page spine cover

END OF TEST

/ 26

Test 5

You have **10 minutes** to do this test. Work as quickly and accurately as you can.

Read this passage carefully and answer the questions that follow.

Animal Migration

Many different animals periodically travel from their birthplace to new destinations, sometimes thousands of kilometres away. This activity has been observed in birds, fish and insects, amongst other animals, and it is often motivated by a search for food. It's likely that migration has been taking place for
5 millions of years, with the oldest surviving written record of it dating as far back as 1000 BCE.

Identifying the exact path that animal migrants take is a tricky business, but modern technology can help. These days, scientists are able to collect information on just how far some animals travel. They can do this by attaching an electronic
10 tag, often called a *geolocator,* to an animal. The geolocator is able to record data such as light levels and the time, and this data is used to suggest where the animal has been.

Birds make the longest migrations of any animal. The arctic tern makes a mammoth southbound journey, flying an average of 35,000 km from the Arctic to
15 the Antarctic, before flying back again. The sooty shearwater makes a round trip that can reach over 60,000 km, and the bar-tailed godwit is famed for making the longest nonstop flight of any bird — over 10,000 km.

But it's not only birds that make long migrations; the humpback whale makes the longest journey of any mammal. It travels up to 10,000 km to warmer water
20 to breed, before making the trip back to the polar regions, where food is more abundant. The monarch butterfly holds the record for the longest insect migration, travelling over 4,000 km to escape the winter temperatures of its home.

Understanding why animals migrate and where they go is far less baffling than establishing how they manage these incredible feats of travel. Stopping en route
25 to refuel is an option; animals that do this are known as *passage migrants*. For example, black terns and hoopoes rest in the UK during spring and autumn.

No matter how animals cope with the trip, their stamina in the face of what can be a perilous journey is truly remarkable.

Answer these questions about the text that you've just read.
Circle the letter that matches the correct answer.

1. How long ago was the oldest surviving record of animal migration written?

   A Millions of years ago

   B Roughly 3,000 years ago

   C Roughly 1,750 years ago

   D Roughly 1,000 years ago

2. According to the text, what does a geolocator aim to do?

   A Provide precise information about migration habits

   B Time how long an animal has been travelling for

   C Record an estimate of the journey made by a migrating animal

   D Track the sun's trajectory

3. According to the text, which animal makes the longest round-trip migration?

   A Sooty shearwater

   B Arctic tern

   C Bar-tailed godwit

   D Humpback whale

4. Which of the following isn't given as a reason for animal migration?

   A Looking for food

   B Moving to a more suitable climate

   C Moving to breeding grounds

   D Natural instinct

5. Which of the following birds are definitely not passage migrants?

A Arctic terns

B Sooty shearwaters

C Bar-tailed godwits

D Black terns

6. Which of the following is not mentioned in the text?

A How often migration takes place

B The direction an arctic tern flies in

C Where a geolocator might be found on an animal

D Which insect is believed to migrate the furthest

7. According to the text, which of the following must be true?

A The monarch butterfly prefers warmer climates.

B Animals are less likely to breed in cool waters.

C Hoopoes cannot be found in the UK in winter.

D No species of reptile migrates.

Mark the word outside the brackets that has a similar meaning to the words in both sets of brackets.

Example: (twig branch) (fasten attach) glue stick affix bough

8. (flee run)	(fasten secure)	lock bolt jog rivet
9. (intellect brain)	(baby-sit supervise)	tend imagination mind sense
10. (sour acidic)	(resentful hateful)	bitter mean severe disagreeable
11. (type sort)	(friendly considerate)	class variety obliging kind

12. (twig bough) (office department) stick studio branch shop

13. (exit depart) (absence holiday) quit rest leave break

14. (bat cudgel) (society group) baton club bar association

Complete the word on the right so that it means the opposite, or nearly the opposite, of the word on the left.

Example: heavy [l][i][g][h][t]

15. disallow [a][c][ ][ ][ ][t]

16. break [ ][e][ ][a][ ][r]

17. plain [o][r][ ][ ][ ][e]

18. enormous [ ][ ][ ][i][s][c][ ][l][e]

19. idle [a][c][ ][ ][ ][ ]

20. invaluable [ ][ ][r][ ][ ][l][e][s][s]

END OF TEST

/ 20

Puzzles 1

Time for a break! These puzzles are a great way to practise your **vocabulary** skills.

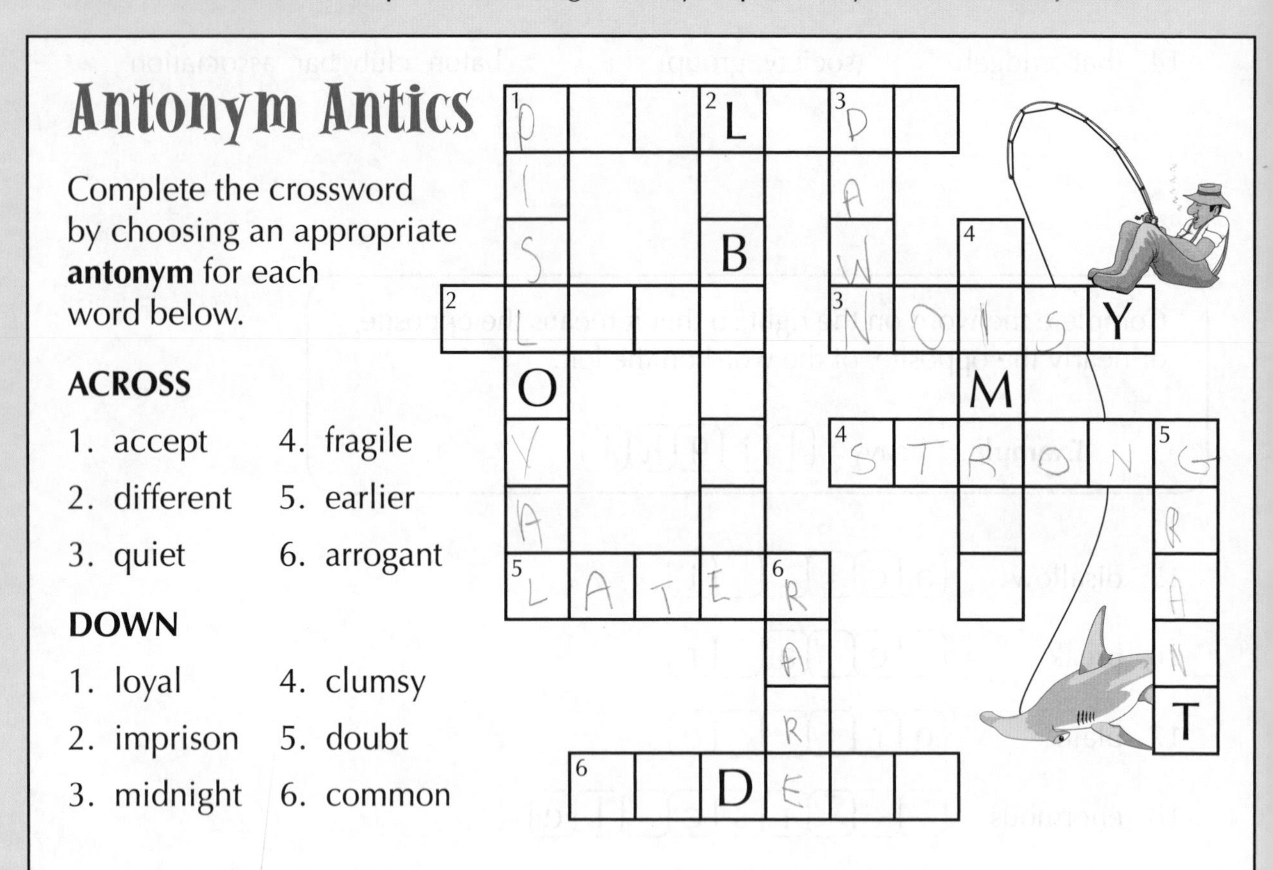

Antonym Antics

Complete the crossword by choosing an appropriate **antonym** for each word below.

ACROSS

1. accept
2. different
3. quiet
4. fragile
5. earlier
6. arrogant

DOWN

1. loyal
2. imprison
3. midnight
4. clumsy
5. doubt
6. common

Spell and Unscramble

Each word below is misspelt. First, cross out the wrong letters, then rearrange the wrong letters into an antonym for the word **lack**.

Watch out — there may be more than one wrong letter per word.

o b b j e c t   u n n h a b i t

i n n d e p e n d a n t   s h a r c k

a p o l o d g y   t e m p a r e t u r e

Antonym of **lack**: ______________________

Test 6

You have **10 minutes** to do this test. Work as quickly and as accurately as you can.

Fill in the missing letters to complete the words in the following passage.

1. Blackpool Tower is a 158 m _ t _ _ high tower located in Blackpool.
2. The design of the tower, which is a popular t _ _ r i _ t attraction,
3. was initially _ _ s p _ _ e d by the Eiffel Tower in Paris. It was
4. c _ n _ t _ u _ t e d between 1891 and 1894. Approximately
5. 2,500 t o _ _ _ s of iron and over five million bricks were used in the
6. tower's s _ _ u _ t _ r e. On its first day of opening on
7. 14th May 1894, the tower had over three thousand v _ s _ t _ _ s.
8. Unfortunately, due to the tower not being painted _ _ o _ e _ l y,
9. the steelwork became _ a _ a _ e d, and the tower had to be rebuilt
10. between 1921 and 1924. Normally dark red in c _ l _ _ r, the top of
11. the tower was painted silver in 1977, in h o n _ _ _ of the Queen's

    Silver Jubilee, and in 1994, the sides of the tower were painted gold
12. to mark the one hundredth a n _ i _ e _ s _ r y of its opening.

Find the word that means the same, or nearly the same, as the word on the left.

Example: **wide** flat straight broad long

13. **disgust** gruesome revulsion shock malice

14. **taunt** renounce ostracise ridicule teasing

15. **angry** fury perturbed aghast indignant

16. **hinder** impede circumvent prohibit assist

17. **excess** difference extend plenty surplus

Mark the word outside the brackets that has a similar meaning to the words in both sets of brackets.

Example: (twig branch) (fasten attach) glue stick affix bough

18. (slim thin) (bend tilt) lean incline gaunt slender

19. (business trade) (habit tradition) custom routine shop norm

20. (quick speedy) (secured stable) mobile fixed attached fast

21. (display monitor) (test examine) auditor image screen trial

Complete the word on the right so that it means the opposite, or nearly the opposite, of the word on the left.

Example: heavy [l][i][g][h][t]

22. pompous [ ][ ][d][ ][s][t]

23. banned [ ][u][t][ ][o][r][ ][s][ ][d]

24. regular [ ][c][c][ ][s][ ][o][n][ ][l]

25. reduce [ ][ ][ ][r][e][ ][s][e]

26. next [ ][r][e][ ][ ][ ][u][s]

END OF TEST

/ 26

Test 7

You have **10 minutes** to do this test. Work as quickly and as accurately as you can.

Read this passage carefully and answer the questions that follow.

The Lonely House

I know some lonely houses off the road
A robber 'd like the look of, —
Wooden barred,
And windows hanging low,
5 Inviting to
A portico*,
Where two could creep:
One hand the tools,
The other peep
10 To make sure all's asleep.
Old-fashioned eyes,
Not easy to surprise!

How orderly the kitchen 'd look by night,
With just a clock, —
15 But they could gag the tick,
And mice won't bark;
And so the walls don't tell,
None will.

A pair of spectacles ajar just stir —
20 An almanac's** aware.
Was it the mat winked,
Or a nervous star?
The moon slides down the stair
To see who's there.

25 There's plunder, — where?
Tankard, or spoon,
Earring, or stone,
A watch, some ancient brooch
To match the grandmamma,
30 Staid*** sleeping there.

Day rattles, too,
Stealth's slow;
The sun has got as far
As the third sycamore.
35 Screams chanticleer****,
"Who's there?"
And echoes, trains away,
Sneer — "Where?"
While the old couple, just astir,
40 Fancy the sunrise left the door ajar!

Emily Dickinson

* portico — *porch*
** almanac — *a type of calendar*
*** staid — *respectable*
**** chanticleer — *cockerel*

Answer these questions about the text that you've just read.
Circle the letter that matches the correct answer.

1. According to the poem, which of these is not given as a reason why the house attracts the burglars?

   A It has windows that are easy to access.
   B Wealthy people live there.
   C It is far from the road.
   D The occupants are sleeping.

2. Which of these words best describes the house?

   A Neglected
   B Secluded
   C Vacant
   D Dilapidated

3. "And mice won't bark; / And so the walls don't tell, / None will." (lines 16-18). What do these lines tell us?

   A The burglars will not leave any evidence of their crime.
   B The burglars are keeping their plans a secret.
   C There are no animals in the house.
   D There is nothing in the house to alert the occupants to intruders.

4. What do the tankard, the spoon, the brooch and the stone have in common?

   A They are the grandfather's possessions.
   B They are items taken by the thieves.
   C They are very old.
   D They are all in the kitchen.

5. What does the word "stealth" (line 32) mean?

A Sneakiness

B Theft

C Sly

D Sunrise

6. Which of these statements is false?

A Two people could fit into the porch.

B The kitchen is very tidy.

C The burglars use tools to get into the house.

D It's dark when the occupants wake up.

7. The poem says "Fancy the sunrise left the door ajar!" (line 40). This tells us that:

A the burglars are still in the house.

B the house's occupants do not know they've been burgled.

C the owners of the house forgot to shut the door.

D the burglars are planning on returning to the house.

Find the word that means the same, or nearly the same, as the word on the left.

Example: **wide** flat straight broad long

8. **careful** accurate passive cautious precise

9. **enthusiastic** exuberant happy motivational obnoxious

10. **bravery** perseverance fortitude arrogance prowess

11. **unusual** eccentric estranged controversial misshapen

12. **notable** infamous obscure dramatic illustrious

13. **boring** tedious persistent tiring dismal

Mark the word outside the brackets that has a similar meaning to the words in both sets of brackets.

Example: (twig branch) (fasten attach) glue stick affix bough

14. (port dock)	(shelter hide)	marine conceal quay harbour
15. (hit spar)	(carton container)	package fight box slap
16. (rubbish waste)	(decline reject)	refuse litter debris disdain
17. (aiming attempting)	(difficult annoying)	trying stressful striving irritating
18. (disagree oppose)	(challenge match)	competition contest game argue
19. (porch lobby)	(enchant mesmerise)	door enthrall entrance bewitch
20. (folder dossier)	(store organise)	sort booklet wallet file

END OF TEST

/ 20

Test 8

You have **10 minutes** to do this test. Work as quickly and as accurately as you can.

Choose the correct words to complete the passage below.

Running is an inexpensive and
1. impervious / inadequate / accessible / opportune
way of keeping fit; the only equipment you need is a pair of
2. competent / suitable / expensive / luxurious
running shoes. Not only can running help in
3. losing / lost / excess / lose
weight, it can also improve psychological health, increase life
4. long / expectancy / opportunities / enjoyment
and develop strength in joints and bones. However, there are
5. advantages / doubts / exceptions / risks
— runners can
6. observe / experience / allow / achieve
pain and injury, often due to
7. efficient / distinctive / improper / unattainable
technique or an insufficient warm-up. Running too far or too
8. many / enough / rare / frequently
can also make runners more
9. susceptible / likely / danger / regular
to injury.

The body needs time to recover from exercise, so 10. ☐ many ☐ most ☐ novice ☐ those runners in particular are 11. ☐ tend ☐ given ☐ advised ☐ advice to rest regularly and increase their distance 12. ☐ promptly ☐ gradually ☐ dramatically ☐ systematically to reduce the possibility of injury.

Three of the words in each list are linked. Mark the word that is not related to these three.

Example: journal diary <u>textbook</u> notebook

13. roast fillet bake fry

14. consequence debrief aftermath forethought

15. demote declass relegate upgrade

16. viewers spectators onlookers listeners

17. transport carry car ship

Complete the word on the right so that it means the same, or nearly the same, as the word on the left.

Example: scared a f r a i d

18. sole _ _ n _

19. empty _ _ c _ n t

20. witness _ b _ _ _ v e

21. sly _ _ n _ _ n g

Mark the word outside the brackets that has a similar meaning to the words in both sets of brackets.

Example: (twig branch) (fasten attach) glue stick affix bough

22. (eat feed) (touch skim) brush graze scrape forage

23. (flaw blemish) (desert abandon) quit glitch renounce defect

24. (new original) (book story) unique unusual novel fiction

25. (ascribe assign) (feature aspect) attribute apply detail factor

26. (act feat) (use utilise) deed exploit apply success

END OF TEST

/ 26

Test 9

You have **10 minutes** to do this test. Work as quickly and as accurately as you can.

Read this passage carefully and answer the questions that follow.

Concorde

Despite being retired from the skies in 2003, after 27 years of commercial flights, Concorde is still famous today for its supersonic speeds. It was one of only two passenger airliners that could exceed the speed of sound, first achieving this on its 45th test flight on 1st October 1969.

5 With a maximum speed of approximately 1350 mph, or almost a mile every 2.5 seconds, Concorde could make journeys in record time: in 1996, one of the aircraft flew from New York to London in 2 hours 52 minutes and 59 seconds. This was an impressive feat; other airliners took over twice as long to complete the same journey. This flight time improved on Concorde's previous record, set in 1990, by 90 **10** seconds. Concorde's other speed records include its 2003 flight across the United States, from New York to Seattle, in 3 hours 55 minutes and 12 seconds.

However, Concorde's speed came at some cost. The aircraft's fuselage was subjected to large forces when flying supersonically, leading to distortion of the aircraft's structure. Also, because the aircraft exceeded the speed of sound, its **15** movement through the sky caused a sonic boom, a noise like an explosion which could be heard from the ground. This meant that Concorde had to avoid certain routes or reduce its speed when flying over land. Concorde's engines were highly inefficient at low speeds; the aircraft burned two tonnes of fuel before it had even left the ground, simply from taxiing to the runway.

20 Only 20 of the aircraft were ever built, with France and the United Kingdom each using seven of them for passenger flights. The remaining aircraft were used only as prototypes and during the development and testing of Concorde. After its retirement — which was brought about due to a combination of low passenger numbers and spiralling maintenance costs — many of the aircraft were displayed in museums **25** across the world. It now seems unlikely that Concorde will ever fly commercially again.

Answer these questions about the text that you've just read.
Circle the letter that matches the correct answer.

1. When did commercial Concorde flights begin?

   A 1969

   B 1976

   C 1990

   D 1996

2. Which of the following statements must be true?

   A No airliner except Concorde has exceeded the speed of sound.

   B The speed of sound is less than 1350 mph.

   C Concorde only made international journeys.

   D Concorde was designed in 1970.

3. In 1992, what was Concorde's flight-time record for the journey from New York to London?

   A 2 hours 54 minutes and 29 seconds

   B 2 hours 52 minutes and 59 seconds

   C 2 hours 51 minutes and 28 seconds

   D 3 hours 55 minutes and 12 seconds

4. Which of these statements cannot be true?

   A Concorde was a passenger airline used for commercial flights.

   B Concorde had to maintain a constant speed from take-off to landing.

   C Concorde was most famous for the speed at which it travelled.

   D Passengers travelled by taxi in order to board the plane on the runway.

5. When could Concorde not fly supersonically?

A When it was over the Atlantic Ocean

B During test flights

C During commercial flights

D While it was over land

6. How many Concorde aircraft were never used for commercial flights?

A 6

B 7

C 13

D 14

7. According to the text, what caused Concorde to be removed from service?

A Structural issues with the aircraft

B Complaints about sonic booms

C Problems with fuel efficiency

D It became too expensive

In each question below, the words can be rearranged to form a sentence. One word doesn't fit in the sentence. Underline the word that doesn't fit.

Example: red the has <u>ride</u> girl bicycle a

8. their brought a waiter food the long bring took to time

9. to snow through friends they wanted the walk his

10. before she to big which race have wanted a the breakfast

11. morning said out time they she at was the

12. thing of right type get those tends to this he

13. they is how why want know to happened and it

14. noticed usual that than expect busier city she the was

Find the word that means the opposite, or nearly the opposite, of the word on the left.

Example: **first** later <u>last</u> next beginning

15. **clear** disjointed cohesive cryptic transparent

16. **real** dubious awry ambiguous counterfeit

17. **planned** automatic spontaneous voluntary casual

18. **disgusting** virtuous honourable delectable frivolous

19. **immoral** ethical humble amiable benevolent

20. **thrive** wither repudiate evade abhor

END OF TEST

/ 20

Test 10

You have **10 minutes** to do this test. Work as quickly and as accurately as you can.

Choose the correct words to complete the passage below.

Every year, millions of people travel to the Canary Islands, a group of volcanic islands

1. ☐ towards ☐ situated ☐ placed ☐ in

off the southwest

2. ☐ coast ☐ island ☐ sea ☐ bank

of Morocco. The islands are part of Spain,

3. ☐ regardless ☐ despite ☐ while ☐ although

they are closer to Africa than

4. ☐ mainland ☐ the rest ☐ peninsula ☐ remainder

Spain.

The Canary Islands, often

5. ☐ named ☐ called ☐ designated ☐ referred

to as simply 'The Canaries', are an extremely

6. ☐ lamentable ☐ popular ☐ affectionate ☐ enigmatic

tourist destination all year round, as they maintain a

7. ☐ mild ☐ required ☐ requisite ☐ desired

climate even

8. ☐ throughout ☐ apart from ☐ between ☐ among

the winter months. Many tourists choose to visit the islands' beaches for a

9. ☐ intense ☐ leisurely ☐ alluring ☐ mundane

holiday, while others

10. ☐ proffer
☐ enjoy
☐ opt
☐ are

to explore the various natural attractions, such as Teide National Park

in Tenerife, home to Mount Teide. The

11. ☐ summit
☐ ascent
☐ elevation
☐ altitude

of this 3,718 m high volcano

is the highest point in Spain, and it is also the third highest volcano in the world when

measured from its

12. ☐ bass
☐ base
☐ ground
☐ level

on the ocean floor.

Complete the word on the right so that it means the opposite, or nearly the opposite, of the word on the left.

Example: heavy [l][i][g][h][t]

13. join [ ][i][s][ ][ ][n][ ][e][c][t]

14. inexact [p][r][ ][ ][i][ ][e]

15. flawed [ ][e][r][ ][e][ ][t]

16. pacify [ ][ ][r][a][g][ ]

17. prosper [l][a][ ][g][ ][i][s][ ]

Mark the word outside the brackets that has a similar meaning to the words in both sets of brackets.

Example: (twig branch) (fasten attach) glue stick affix bough

18. (shine buff) (perfect refine) varnish polish improve enhance
19. (limit restrict) (cover top) cap curtail crown curb
20. (push squeeze) (urge compel) impel crush drive press
21. (gesture signal) (proposal suggestion) sign idea motion movement
22. (remove take) (excerpt passage) snippet quotation extract remove

In each question below, the words can be rearranged to form a sentence. One word doesn't fit in the sentence. Underline the word that doesn't fit.

Example: red the has ride girl bicycle a

23. book entire by read need I began to the tomorrow
24. an saw few the we people very late shop a leaving
25. don't tell do said you me what need to should I
26. promises Tina keep doesn't break always intend to she makes

END OF TEST

/ 26

Puzzles 2

There are two puzzles on this page that are bound to give your brain a workout.

Find the Secret Message

Find the two words that should be swapped in order for each sentence to make sense. Underline both words and write them in the box below.

Rearrange the words you've underlined to reveal a secret message.

1. The robbers broke in at gold and stole the queen's midnight.
2. Hopefully the order delivered be will on Tuesday morning.
3. At clown the Jane's party was very funny.
4. Mum's pork be will eventually medallions ready to eat.

Secret message: ______________________________

______________________________.

Wordy Wisdom

Solve the clues to find out something about Harry the hippo.

a. Find a multiple of four whose letters are in alphabetical order.

b. Replace the first letter of your answer with the letter that's nine places ahead of 'J' in the alphabet.

c. Add a letter that sounds like a vegetable between the first two letters.

Answer: Harry isn't very ________________.

Test 11

You have **10 minutes** to do this test. Work as quickly and accurately as you can.

Fill in the missing letters to complete the words in the following passage.

1. A discussion about how many days [_ h e _ _] are in a year might refer to
2. *common years* and *leap years*. A common year [_ o n _ _ s t _] of
3. 365 days, [w _ e _ e _ s] a leap year has 366 days. The extra day found
4. in a leap year occurs every four years on 29th February. The [_ e a _ o _]
5. we have leap years is connected to the Earth's [_ o t _ _ i o n] around
6. the Sun. The Earth takes fractionally [_ o n _ e _] than 365 days to circle
7. the Sun: in fact, it takes 365 days, 5 hours, 48 [_ _ _ _ t e s] and 46
8. seconds for it to complete an orbit. If leap years didn't [_ x _ _ t], almost
9. six hours a year would be lost. This might not [_ _ u _ d] like much, but in
10. 100 years time, without leap years, our [_ a l _ n d _ _ s] would be
11. wrong by [_ p _ r _ x _ m a t _ l y] twenty-four days. Adding
12. an extra day to February every four years [_ _ k _ s] up for the time lost.

Three of the words in each list are linked. Mark the word that is not related to these three.

Example: journal diary <u>textbook</u> notebook

13. dwelling household residence lodgings

14. drought thirstily quench hungry

15. thin sleek streamlined aerodynamic

16. royal princely ladylike regal

17. cascade scale ascend escalate

Complete the word on the right so that it means the same, or nearly the same, as the word on the left.

Example: scared a f r a i d

18. co-worker c o l l e _ _ _ e

19. similarity r e _ e m b l _ n _ e

20. search r a _ _ a k

21. unfriendly _ o _ _ _ l e

22. problem d i _ _ _ _ a

In each question below, the words can be rearranged to form a sentence. One word doesn't fit in the sentence. Underline the word that doesn't fit.

Example: red the has <u>ride</u> girl bicycle a

23. keep begin journey themselves on they to entertained long had the

24. to the pupils was proposal banned most ban by homework supported

25. lifted house of crane the on above their bricks top

26. had perform great show in review paper the our school a

END OF TEST

/ 26

Test 12

You have **10 minutes** to do this test. Work as quickly and accurately as you can.

Read this passage carefully and answer the questions that follow.

Alfred Wainwright

Alfred Wainwright was an author and an illustrator who delighted, informed and inspired fellwalkers for decades with his guides to the Lake District fells*.

Born in Blackburn, Lancashire, in 1907, Wainwright lived with his parents and three siblings. His father was a stonemason, but he was often unemployed. Despite
5 being academically gifted, Wainwright left school aged 13. Unlike other boys his age, he avoided having to work in the mills and was employed as an office worker for Blackburn council. He attended night school and gained qualifications which provided him with opportunities to advance.

Wainwright went to the Lake District for the very first time when he was 23. He
10 climbed a hill near lake Windermere and was astounded by the view of the fells, the trees and the lake below. What he saw was in stark contrast to the industrial town he lived in. This trip started his life-long passion for the Lake District. In 1941, he moved to the area and spent much of his spare time walking in the fells. Over the years, he developed an excellent knowledge of the area.

15 In 1952, he began writing the books for which he was most famous: his seven pictorial guides to the Lake District, which took 13 years to complete. He described them as his 'love letter' to the Lakeland fells. They give incredibly accurate and detailed information about 214 fells in the Lake District, including handwritten route descriptions and hand-drawn maps, diagrams and pictures. The fells in these
20 books are known as 'Wainwrights' and many walkers set themselves the challenge of ascending all of these fells over their lifetime.

Wainwright's favourite fell was Haystacks, and it was here that his ashes were scattered after his death in 1991.

* fell — *hill*

Answer these questions about the text that you've just read.
Circle the letter that matches the correct answer.

1. Who is the target audience of Wainwright's books?

   A People who were born in Lancashire

   B Rambling enthusiasts

   C People in industrial work

   D People who live in the Lake District

2. Which word below best describes Wainwright's upbringing?

   A Destitute

   B Privileged

   C Humble

   D Abusive

3. Why was Wainwright able to progress in his career?

   A He had experience as a council worker.

   B He became more qualified.

   C He learnt stonemasonry from his father.

   D He was well travelled.

4. What sparked Wainwright's interest in the Lake District?

   A The similarities between Blackburn and the Lake District

   B The area he took up residence in in 1941

   C The time he spent near Windermere aged 23

   D The sight of the Lake District lakes

5. How old was Wainwright when he completed his guides?

A 34 years old

B 45 years old

C 84 years old

D 58 years old

6. What does the breadth and detail of his books tell us about Wainwright?

A He intended to spend 13 years writing the books.

B He was extremely committed to the Lake District fells.

C His description of each fell required multiple pages.

D He aimed to include multiple versions of the maps and diagrams.

7. Why do you think some fells have become known as 'Wainwrights'?

A The success of his books has made his name synonymous with them.

B It was organised as a tribute to him following his death.

C He discovered them and gave his name to them.

D It's easier than remembering their proper names.

Complete the word on the right so that it means the opposite, or nearly the opposite, of the word on the left.

Example: heavy [l][i][g][h][t]

8. leader [ ][ ][l][ ][o][w][ ][r]

9. modern [ ][ ][t][m][ ][d][ ][d]

10. sorrowful [e][ ][u][b][ ][r][ ][n][t]

11. anger [a][p][ ][ ][ ][s][e]

12. build [ ][ ][m][o][ ][i][s][ ]

13. planned [i][ ][p][u][ ][s][ ][ ][e]

14. aggravate [a][l][ ][e][v][ ][ ][t][e]

Three of the words in each list are linked. Mark the word that is not related to these three.

Example: journal diary textbook notebook

15. player domino counter card

16. support back comfort endorse

17. chair director leader seat

18. instruct enquire command insist

19. clatter murmur crash racket

20. highway road motorway pavement

END OF TEST

/ 20

Test 13

You have **10 minutes** to do this test. Work as quickly and accurately as you can.

Fill in the missing letters to complete the words in the following passage.

1. On Shrove Tuesday, the day before the [ ][t][ ][ ][t] of Lent, lots of people
2. will [i][ ][d][ ][l][ ][e] in a warm and tasty pancake. Whether sweet or
3. [s][ ][v][ ][ ][r][y], there are countless ways pancakes can be eaten, but
4. the basic [i][n][g][r][ ][ ][ ][ ][n][t][s] for the batter are usually
5. the same. As long as you have flour, milk and eggs, [ ][l][ ][s] a bit of oil or
6. butter for the pan, you can [ ][a][ ][e] a pancake. Before you start cooking
7. however, you might want to do a bit of [p][r][ ][ ][ ][r][a][ ][i][o][n].
8. Pancakes can be [t][ ][i][ ][k][y] to keep warm once they're cooked, so it's
9. [w][ ][ ][ ][h] planning ahead if you've got the time. Lay the table in
10. [ ][d][ ][ ][n][ ][e] and prepare the toppings, such as chopped fruit or
11. [ ][r][ ][t][ ][d] cheese. Then, as soon as your pancake is cooked, you can
12. [ ][s][s][ ][m][b][ ][ ] it and enjoy!

Mark the word outside the brackets that has a similar meaning to the words in both sets of brackets.

Example: (twig branch) (fasten attach) glue stick affix bough

13. (dish meal) (route direction) trail path food course
14. (rearrange mix) (shamble straggle) stumble reorder shuffle jumble
15. (establish start) (discovered located) found initiate spotted form
16. (allure appeal) (spell incantation) draw witchcraft hex charm
17. (hint shred) (copy sketch) draw trace remnant clue

In each question below, the words can be rearranged to form a sentence. One word doesn't fit in the sentence. Underline the word that doesn't fit.

Example: red the has ride girl bicycle a

18. scared brother of my is dentist to teeth going the
19. until Julie days was counting number her down holiday the
20. garden in smell the are beautiful flowers your looking
21. smashed very not the to Michael vase careful china was break
22. start back return is heading it time camp to towards

Find the word that means the opposite, or nearly the opposite, of the word on the left.

Example: **first** later <u>last</u> next beginning

23. **calm** placid agitated ferocious insistent

24. **honest** intrepid blunt insincere candid

25. **absurd** irrelevant bizarre reasonable secondary

26. **uneducated** bewildered sonorous experienced academic

END OF TEST

/ 26

Test 14

You have **10 minutes** to do this test. Work as quickly and accurately as you can.

Read this passage carefully and answer the questions that follow.

Adapted from 'Story of the Bandbox'

Up to the age of sixteen, at a private school and afterwards at one of those great institutions for which England is justly famous, Mr. Harry Hartley had received the ordinary education of a gentleman. At that period he manifested a remarkable distaste for study; and his only surviving parent being both weak and ignorant, he
5 was permitted thenceforward to spend his time in the attainment of petty and purely elegant accomplishments. Two years later, he was left an orphan and almost a beggar. For all active and industrious pursuits, Harry was unfitted alike by nature and training. He could sing romantic ditties, and accompany himself with discretion on the piano; he was a graceful although a timid cavalier*; he had a pronounced
10 taste for chess; and nature had sent him into the world with one of the most engaging exteriors that can well be fancied. Blond and pink, with dove's eyes and a gentle smile, he had an air of agreeable tenderness and melancholy and the most submissive and caressing manners. But when all is said, he was not the man to lead armaments of war or direct the councils of a State.

15 A fortunate chance and some influence obtained for Harry, at the time of his bereavement, the position of private secretary to Major-General Sir Thomas Vandeleur, C.B. Sir Thomas was a man of sixty, loud-spoken, boisterous, and domineering. For some reason, some service the nature of which had been often whispered and repeatedly denied, the Rajah of Kashgar had presented this officer
20 with the sixth known diamond of the world. The gift transformed General Vandeleur from a poor into a wealthy man, from an obscure and unpopular soldier into one of the lions of London society.

* cavalier — *horseman*

Robert Louis Stevenson

Answer these questions about the text that you've just read.
Circle the letter that matches the correct answer.

1. How did Harry feel about education?

   A He thought it was great.

   B He found it boring.

   C He didn't like studying.

   D He neither loved nor hated it.

2. Why was Harry able to spend his time on leisure pursuits?

   A His parent wasn't strong-minded enough to stop him.

   B Elegant accomplishments were considered more important.

   C It was part of the ordinary life of a gentleman.

   D He was remarkably intelligent and didn't need to study.

3. How do you know that Harry relied on his guardian for financial support?

   A He was able to go to a famous university.

   B He needed money to finance his many hobbies.

   C His income dried up after the death of his parent.

   D He often went horse riding, which is an expensive sport.

4. According to the text, which of the following must be true?

   A Harry had wanted a job in the army.

   B Harry was not well-suited to the world of work.

   C Employers did not appreciate Harry's skills.

   D Harry was unable to sing and play the piano at the same time.

5. How did Harry become Sir Thomas's private secretary?

   A On account of his handsome appearance

   B Through a stroke of luck and his connections

   C Due to his unsuitability for leadership roles

   D Because Sir Thomas had sympathy for Harry's situation

6. Why did the Rajah of Kashgar give Sir Thomas a diamond?

   A Sir Thomas had done the Rajah a favour.

   B Because Sir Thomas intimidated the Rajah of Kashgar.

   C The Rajah wanted to make Sir Thomas a popular man.

   D We don't know — it's a secret.

7. Owning the Rajah's diamond made Sir Thomas:

   A very arrogant.

   B a very important person.

   C unappreciative of the value of money.

   D the bravest man in London.

In each question below, the words can be rearranged to form a sentence. One word doesn't fit in the sentence. Underline the word that doesn't fit.

Example: red the has <u>ride</u> girl bicycle a

8. in weekend read book two she the days whole

9. singing the perched tweet branch bird was a while on

10. miles exhibition Gethin of travelled twenty see hundreds to the

11. thinking I Australia visiting of am on to going holiday

12. leave when switched the home remember off turn to lights you

13. outline Rina will pencil sketched an in a house of

14. influx sun an good there tourists of was thanks weather to the

Complete the word on the right so that it means the same, or nearly the same, as the word on the left.

Example: scared a f r a i d

15. summit p _ _ n _ c l e

16. unacceptable d _ _ l o r _ b l e

17. naughty _ i s o b _ d _ e _ t

18. convince p _ r s _ a d _

19. boring t _ d _ o _ s

20. hopeful _ _ t i m _ s t _ c

END OF TEST

/ 20

Test 15

You have **10 minutes** to do this test. Work as quickly and accurately as you can.

Read this passage carefully and answer the questions that follow.

The Enigma Machine

In times of war, army divisions need to communicate discretely. If an enemy intercepts a message, the consequences can be catastrophic. To overcome this danger, in 1928, the German Army acquired a device that intended to transmit information securely. The device was called the Enigma machine.

5 The Enigma machine was invented by Arthur Scherbius, a German engineer who patented his creation in 1919. Originally designed for commercial use, the Enigma machine was a scrambling device that translated messages into codes and codes into messages. Most models consisted of a keyboard, a panel of lights which looked just like the keyboard, and several rotating wheels (or rotors) located above the panel.

10 Once entrusted with a message, an Enigma machine operator adjusted the settings for the rotors. The operator then encoded the message by noting down the letters that lit up on the panel of lights when the correspondence was keyed into the keyboard. The Enigma machine substituted each letter with a different letter, which resulted in a nonsensical series of words. The operator communicated this gibberish to another

15 operator, who also had to have an Enigma machine. The recipient adjusted their rotors to match those of the sender by consulting a codebook which set out the daily settings. He or she then repeated the process to decipher the encrypted text.

The German Army believed unreservedly that the Enigma machine was secure and used it in the run-up to and during World War II. However, its security was breached

20 when Hans-Thilo Schmidt, a spy working for the French who held a position at Germany's cipher office in Berlin, shared information about the Enigma machine with Marian Rejewski, a Polish code breaker. Schmidt's insights coupled with Rejewski's equations enabled the Polish to decipher messages produced using the Enigma machine, a feat that would have an important bearing on the outcome of the war.

Answer these questions about the text that you've just read.
Circle the letter that matches the correct answer.

1. What dangers do intercepted messages pose?

A They disregard a breach in security.

B They can give an advantage to the enemy.

C They identify a country's enemy.

D They delay communications between army divisions.

2. What was the Enigma machine?

A A piece of equipment that was used universally by the military

B An invention that encoded jargonistic texts

C A device that decoded correspondence with discretion

D A device that enciphered and deciphered sensitive messages

3. Who did Arthur Scherbius intend the Enigma machine to be used by?

A The German Army

B Businesses

C Hans-Thilo Scmidt

D International cipher offices

4. How did Enigma machine operators encode a message?

A They typed a message letter-by-letter, recording the light panel's output.

B They pressed the keys that were illuminated on the light panel.

C They wrote down which keys on the keyboard were used in a message.

D They keyed in letters that replaced the letters in the original message.

5. How did recipients of Enigma correspondence decode the text?

A They used the sender's Enigma machine, but altered its settings.

B They decoded it on paper and entered the result into the Enigma machine.

C They followed the same procedure used to encode the message.

D They put the rotor settings on the Enigma machine into reverse.

6. Why did Hans-Thilo Schmidt have access to information about the Enigma machine?

A He could understand documents written in French.

B He was an expert at infiltrating security systems.

C He worked for a German encoding department.

D He worked in partnership with Marian Rejewski.

7. What did Hans-Thilo Schmidt and Marian Rejewski have in common?

A They had direct access to an Enigma machine.

B They enabled France to translate messages sent by the German Army.

C They were entirely responsible for the war's outcome.

D They worked for countries that were not privy to messages sent by the German Army.

Find the word that means the same, or nearly the same, as the word on the left.

Example: **wide** flat straight broad long

8. **heave** haul weighty shove inaugurate

9. **scrawny** scruffy fickle gaunt small

10. **enthusiasm** thrill fervour hysteria penitence

11. **conflict** tessellation strife debate concord

12. **unstable** volatile insidious reticent vacuous

13. **suppress** immerse hide tactile stifle

14. **charitable** contrived altruistic taciturn poignant

Three of the words in each list are linked. Mark the word that is not related to these three.

Example: journal diary <u>textbook</u> notebook

15. break shatter rest pause

16. throw launch hurl roll

17. confirm propose certify approve

18. hygienic sanitary tidy clean

19. cut incision slice rip

20. origin dawn conclusion outset

END OF TEST

/ 20

Puzzles 3

Time for a break! These puzzles are a great way to practise your **word making** skills.

Word Family Frolics

Five words are hidden in the grid. Each word belongs to the same word family as one of the words below. Circle the words, but make sure you find the correct word type.

Example: Find a noun related to 'skilful'.

a) Find a noun related to 'quick'.

b) Find an adjective related to 'strangely'.

c) Find an adverb related to 'intelligence'.

d) Find a verb related to 'runner'.

e) Find a verb related to 'courier'.

R	S	U	T	H	F	R	C
E	P	N	A	Y	P	E	L
L	E	W	B	X	O	V	E
C	E	E	I	A	D	I	V
H	D	I	L	J	Z	L	E
S	P	R	I	N	T	E	R
A	O	D	T	B	S	D	L
K	G	E	Y	V	Y	I	Y

Double Trouble

Solve the clues below to find three words that mean something different when they are spelled backwards.

a) Forwards I come after main courses. Backwards I am anxious.

_ _ _ _ _ _ _ _

b) Forwards I exist. Backwards I am wicked.

_ _ _ _

c) Forwards I am a celebrity. Backwards I am some rodents.

_ _ _ _

Test 16

You have **10 minutes** to do this test. Work as quickly and as accurately as you can.

Choose the correct words to complete the passage below.

During the Second World War, food rationing was

1. ☐ provided ☐ introduced ☐ designated ☐ administer

, meaning the amount of food families could receive was

2. ☐ increased ☐ restricted ☐ addressed ☐ reviewed

.

3. ☐ Notwithstanding ☐ Despite ☐ Although ☐ Indeed

rationing may sound cruel, it was introduced to

4. ☐ avoid ☐ ensure ☐ insure ☐ implement

that everyone had enough food to survive. Before the war, much of Britain's food was

5. ☐ destroyed ☐ luxurious ☐ inedible ☐ imported

; however, once the war began, supply ships were often attacked, leading to a

6. ☐ decline ☐ lessen ☐ subside ☐ depreciate

in the amount of food brought into the country. Food prices could have soared as supplies became 7. ☐ larger ☐ abundant ☐ scarce ☐ fewer , meaning only 8. ☐ limited ☐ wealthy ☐ superior ☐ diverse people

would have been able to 9. ☐ afford ☐ get ☐ receive ☐ provide to eat well. 10. ☐ Therefore ☐ After ☐ Initially ☐ Additionally , rationing

only applied to a 11. ☐ reduced ☐ restricted ☐ valuable ☐ few products such as bacon, butter and sugar. As the war

12. ☐ began ☐ maintained ☐ progressed ☐ spread , however, rationing was extended to include many other foods.

Find the word that means the opposite, or nearly the opposite, of the word on the left.

Example: **first** later <u>last</u> next beginning

13. **necessary** obscure obligatory redundant surplus

14. **incomplete** exhaustive long-winded precise prolonged

15. **cheerful** disillusioned isolated dubious despondent

16. **unwise** expert proficient prudent enlightened

17. **confidence** intimidation humility aversion apprehension

In each question below, the words can be rearranged to form a sentence. One word doesn't fit in the sentence. Underline the word that doesn't fit.

Example: red the has <u>ride</u> girl bicycle a

18. before it adult grown long all be you're won't up

19. wait next have we until suppose to I will tomorrow

20. invite unfair it we him will if be would didn't

21. their towards set beach they on off walk the to long down

Three of the words in each list are linked. Mark the word that is not related to these three.

Example: journal diary <u>textbook</u> notebook

22. glove shoe slipper sock

23. lights bauble holly tinsel

24. recover cure treat operate

25. department division company section

26. guitar string wind brass

END OF TEST

/26

Test 17

You have **10 minutes** to do this test. Work as quickly and as accurately as you can.

Read this passage carefully and answer the questions that follow.

Marie Curie

Marie Curie's scientific achievements made her one of the most famous scientists of the nineteenth and twentieth centuries. Her research impacted not only the fields of physics and chemistry, but also medical science, such as cancer treatment.

The youngest of five children, Curie was born in Poland in November 1867. As it
5 was illegal for women to go to university in Poland, Curie moved to France in 1891 to study at the University of Paris. Once there, she lived with her sister Bronya, who financed her education, as Marie had done for her. In July 1893, Curie obtained a degree in physics, and then her second degree a year later. In 1894, Curie met fellow physicist Pierre Curie, with whom she worked closely, and married in 1895.
10 One of their most notable discoveries was that of radium, a substance that was later used for sterilising infected wounds and in the treatment of cancer.

In 1903, Curie was awarded the Nobel Prize in Physics for her discoveries. She was the first woman ever to achieve this prestigious award. She was also the first female professor at the University of Paris, succeeding her husband's position after
15 he died in an accident in 1906. She received her second Nobel Prize, this time in chemistry, in 1911, making her the first person to win twice. These were ground-breaking accomplishments, as women were often shunned from education and the field of science at the time.

After the First World War broke out in 1914, Curie's work was put on hold as she
20 put all of her efforts into the treatment of wounded soldiers. She created mobile X-ray units which she used on the front line, enabling her to quickly diagnose injuries such as gunshot wounds and broken bones, saving many lives.

In 1930, the Marie Curie Hospital opened in the UK, offering cancer treatments that Curie's discoveries had made possible. This hospital eventually became a
25 cancer care charity which still operates today.

Answer these questions about the text that you've just read.
Circle the letter that matches the correct answer.

1. Why did Marie Curie move to Paris?

A To live with her husband.

B It was possible for women to go to university there.

C She didn't want to study in Poland.

D She could earn more money in France.

2. Which of these statements cannot be true?

A Bronya was younger than Marie.

B Bronya and Marie both left Poland.

C Marie had four siblings.

D Bronya studied at the University of Paris.

3. How old was Marie Curie when she received her first degree?

A 25

B 26

C 28

D 27

4. According to the text, which of these statements must be true?

A Curie was the first female professor in France.

B Curie is the only person to date to have won two Nobel Prizes.

C Pierre Curie was a professor at the time of his death.

D Curie is the only woman to have ever won a Nobel Prize.

5. Which of the following occurred before Pierre's death?

A World War One began.

B Marie became the first female professor at the University of Paris.

C Marie received the Nobel Prize in Chemistry.

D Marie received the Nobel Prize in Physics.

6. Which of the following does the text not attribute to Marie Curie?

A Contributions to cancer treatment

B The first female Nobel Prize winner

C The discovery of X-rays

D The discovery of radium

7. Why was a hospital named after Marie Curie?

A It treated cancer based on Curie's research.

B It was in her hometown.

C It used her X-ray units.

D To celebrate her second Nobel Prize win.

Mark the word outside the brackets that has a similar meaning to the words in both sets of brackets.

Example: (twig branch) (fasten attach) glue <u>stick</u> affix bough

8. (transport move) (boat ferry) load ship lift freight

9. (transparent see-through) (obvious explicit) light evident sight clear

10. (crushed powdered) (floor earth) soil ground base grated

11. (vex irk) (foil thwart) madden defeat frustrate annoy

12. (daring heroic) (endure confront) defy fearless brave withstand

13. (collapse pass out) (indistinct unclear) faint weak unsteady shaky

14. (payment instalment) (put place) sum position deposit amount

In each question below, the words can be rearranged to form a sentence. One word doesn't fit in the sentence. Underline the word that doesn't fit.

Example: red the has <u>ride</u> girl bicycle a

15. to before I teeth sleeping always my going brush bed

16. the well yesterday hope interview that I goes tomorrow

17. cakes had weekend he at always cook baking enjoyed the

18. on aren't year holiday my planning going friends abroad this

19. never have they innocent completely I that thought were she

20. days snow the it closed because three school for was of

END OF TEST

/ 20

Test 18

You have **10 minutes** to do this test. Work as quickly and as accurately as you can.

Fill in the missing letters to complete the words in the following passage.

1. With an _l_v_t_on of 8,848 metres, Mount Everest is the
2. highest mountain on the planet. This fact has e_t_c_d many
3. mountaineers to attempt the dangerous _xp_dit_o_ to the
4. mountain's su__i_. Aside from the dangers of avalanches, falls and
5. frostbite, the lack of oxygen at high _lt_t_des can result in
6. unconsciousness and even death. To minimise these _i_k_, climbers
7. undertake intensive training p___r to the climb, and there have been numerous successful attempts to ascend Everest since records began in 1921.
8. However, there is some d__b_ over who exactly achieved this
9. f___ first; in 1924, a group of mountaineers attempted to climb
10. Everest, but they never __t_r_ed. It is thought to be
11. _os__b_e that they reached the top, which would have made them the first people to have done so. To this day, it is unknown
12. w__t_er they succeeded.

Three of the words in each list are linked. Mark the word that is not related to these three.

Example: journal diary <u>textbook</u> notebook

13. initiate instigate sustain begin

14. remember anticipate recall reminisce

15. invite lure attract repel

16. decode encrypt decipher interpret

17. ardent zealous fervent sentimental

Find the word that means the same, or nearly the same, as the word on the left.

Example: **wide** flat straight <u>broad</u> long

18. **amusement** joy jubilation mirth comical

19. **snatch** gather wrest annex clasp

20. **limited** restricted nominal frugal inferior

21. **bleak** callous sorrowful austere desolate

22. **impending** imminent probable hasty intended

Mark the word outside the brackets that has a similar meaning to the words in both sets of brackets.

Example: (twig branch) (fasten attach) glue <u>stick</u> affix bough

23. (expand develop) (intricate detailed) fancy elaborate explain busy

24. (hone improve) (flawless intact) perfect whole refine impeccable

25. (cut prune) (produce harvest) yield shave crop trim

26. (alcove nook) (break interval) recess corner pause niche

END OF TEST

/ 26

Test 19

You have **10 minutes** to do this test. Work as quickly and as accurately as you can.

Read this passage carefully and answer the questions that follow.

The Song of the Camp

"Give us a song!" the soldiers cried,
The outer trenches guarding,
When the heated guns of the camps allied
Grew weary of bombarding.

5 The dark Redan*, in silent scoff,
Lay, grim and threatening, under;
And the tawny mound of the Malakoff**
No longer belched its thunder.

There was a pause. A guardsman said,
10 "We storm the forts to-morrow;
Sing while we may, another day
Will bring enough of sorrow."

They lay along the battery's side,
Below the smoking cannon:
15 Brave hearts, from Severn and from Clyde,
And from the banks of Shannon.

They sang of love, and not of fame;
Forgot was Britain's glory:
Each heart recalled a different name,
20 But all sang "Annie Laurie."

Voice after voice caught up the song,
Until its tender passion
Rose like an anthem, rich and strong, —
Their battle-eve confession.

25 Dear girl, her name he dared not speak,
But, as the song grew louder,
Something upon the soldier's cheek
Washed off the stains of powder.

Beyond the darkening ocean burned
30 The bloody sunset's embers,
While the Crimean valleys learned
How English love remembers.

And once again a fire of hell
Rained on the Russian quarters,
35 With scream of shot, and burst of shell,
And bellowing of the mortars!

And Irish Nora's eyes are dim
For a singer, dumb and gory;
And English Mary mourns for him
40 Who sang of "Annie Laurie."

Sleep, soldiers! still in honoured rest
Your truth and valour wearing:
The bravest are the tenderest, —
The loving are the daring.

by Bayard Taylor

* Redan — *part of a fort*
** Malakoff — *the name of a fort*

Answer these questions about the text that you've just read.
Circle the letter that matches the correct answer.

1. "Grew weary of bombarding" (line 4). What does this line tell us?

   A The guns overheated.

   B The soldiers are angry at having to fight.

   C The soldiers want to call off their attack.

   D The soldiers have been fighting for a long time.

2. Why does the guardsman allow the soldiers to sing?

   A They are bored and have nothing else to do.

   B The soldiers force him to.

   C He wants to postpone the fighting.

   D He wants them to have fun while they have the chance.

3. How do you think the soldiers feel in lines 17-20?

   A Lonely and forlorn

   B Nostalgic and sentimental

   C Pessimistic and neglectful

   D Antagonistic and confrontational

4. What "Washed off the stains of powder" (line 28) from the soldier's cheek?

   A Rain

   B Tears

   C His hand

   D Sweat

5. "And once again a fire of hell / Rained on the Russian quarters" (lines 33-34). What do these lines tell us?

   A The soldiers are fighting amongst themselves.

   B The camp has caught fire.

   C It has started to rain.

   D The battle has resumed.

6. Which line tells the reader where the war is being fought?

   A Brave hearts, from Severn and from Clyde

   B And from the banks of Shannon

   C While the Crimean valleys learned

   D And Irish Nora's eyes are dim

7. What has happened at the end of the poem?

   A The soldiers have gone to sleep.

   B The soldiers have won the battle.

   C Some soldiers have died.

   D The soldiers have started singing again.

Three of the words in each list are linked. Mark the word that is not related to these three.

Example: journal diary <u>textbook</u> notebook

8. hasten amble sprint hurtle

9. lawn garden shrub hedge

10. window wall brick carpet

11. core interior layer centre

12. unfortunate regrettable undesirable precarious

13. bewildered oblivious confused perplexed

Find the word that means the same, or nearly the same, as the word on the left.

Example: **wide** flat straight <u>broad</u> long

14. **supposed** disputed alleged assume fictional

15. **distressing** harrowing daunting gruelling upset

16. **confuse** bewilder enrage agitate contradict

17. **sturdy** dynamic robust vigorous imperative

18. **collect** compile obtained modify regulate

19. **brief** adamant trivial minimal concise

20. **soothe** intervene suppress captivate subdue

END OF TEST

/ 20

Test 20

You have **10 minutes** to do this test. Work as quickly and as accurately as you can.

Fill in the missing letters to complete the words in the following passage.

With air temperatures frequently dropping to –40°C during winter, Antarctica is

1. Earth's coldest continent. Consequently, its n _ t _ v _ animals, such as
2. the emperor penguin, have _ d _ p t _ d to the cold with certain
3. characteristics and behaviours. The birds p _ _ s e _ s a
4. d _ _ s _ coat of oily, overlapping feathers, providing
5. _ f _ _ c t _ v e insulation by trapping air next to the skin.
6. They also have a thick l _ _ _ r of fat to protect them from the cold.
7. An important p _ _ c _ i _ e for emperor penguins is huddling;
8. groups of penguins c l _ s t _ _ together, often with their chicks at
9. the centre, to s _ _ e l _ each other against the bitter wind. The
10. huddle is c _ n s _ _ n _ l y moving, so that penguins
11. a _ _ e r n _ t e between standing in the warmer centre of the
12. huddle and on the o _ t _ _ edge, and they all get to keep warm.

In each question below, the words can be rearranged to form a sentence. One word doesn't fit in the sentence. Underline the word that doesn't fit.

Example: red the has ride girl bicycle a

13. with and my have two milk kettle I sugars coffee
14. swim lakes too much the in was cold pool to
15. broke too couldn't to because she work car down get her
16. escaped yesterday collars dog from afternoon his nearly the park
17. car speeding two police and accident ambulances a went past

Complete the word on the right so that it means the same, or nearly the same, as the word on the left.

Example: scared a f r a i d

18. accurate _ r _ c _ s e
19. obedient _ u _ i _ u l
20. ambition _ s p _ r a t _ o n
21. skill _ x p _ r t _ s e
22. gain _ r _ f _ t

Find the word that means the opposite, or nearly the opposite, of the word on the left.

Example: **first** later <u>last</u> next beginning

23. **friendly** ignorant crude indifferent aloof

24. **hesitant** stubborn opinionated intrusive decisive

25. **polite** bothersome repugnant discourteous sordid

26. **similar** outlandish diverse exceptional erratic

END OF TEST

/ 26

Puzzles 4

Have a break and give this puzzle a go to practise your **word-making** skills.

Compound Conundrums

Nine compound words can be found in the word puzzles below. One part of each word is given for you. Use the clues to find the second part of the words and write the completed compound words on the lines below each puzzle.

Example:

PENCE PENCE
PENCE PENCE
PENCE PENCE

SIXPENCE

Hint: look at what the word is <u>doing</u> or <u>how</u> it's been written. In the example, the word 'pence' has been written six times, so the answer is 'sixpence'.

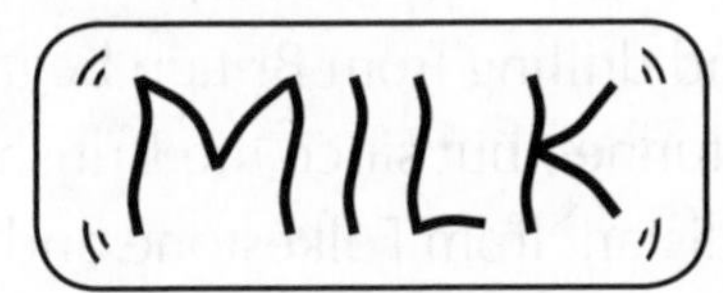

ERIF

___________ ___________ ___________

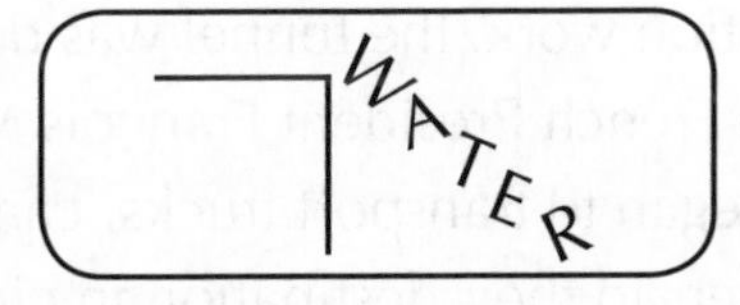

___________ ___________ ___________

___________ ___________ ___________

Test 21

You have **10 minutes** to do this test. Work as quickly and accurately as you can.

Read this passage carefully and answer the questions that follow.

The Channel Tunnel

Deep beneath the earth, some 75 metres at its lowest point, and stretching 31.4 miles from Folkestone, Kent, to Coquelles near Calais, lies an underground passage that whisks passengers under the sea at speeds of up to 99 miles per hour. In fact, a trio of tunnels makes up the Channel Tunnel: two for trains and one for emergency
5 access.

The first suggestion for a cross-Channel connection had been made by Albert Mathieu-Favier, a French mining engineer, in 1802, but 171 years passed before approval for such a structure was granted. Consent came in the form of the Franco-British Channel Tunnel Treaty, signed by Edward Heath and Georges
10 Pompidou, the British Prime Minister and the French President, respectively.

Construction began from the French side in 1988, and drilling from Britain began shortly after. Two years later, the two teams met in the tunnel, but since the British had made greater progress, their meeting was not equidistant from Folkestone and Coquelles. Brandishing blue, red and white flags, Graham Fagg and Phillippe
15 Cozette, two tunnellers, posed triumphantly for publicity shots at this ceremonial breakthrough.

After six years of excavation work, the tunnel was declared officially open by Queen Elizabeth II and the French President François Mitterrand. In staggered succession, shuttle trains began to transport trucks, cars, coaches, motorcycles and
20 caravans, bringing passengers to their destination in circa 35 minutes. Currently, up to 400 trains make the trip every 24 hours, transporting around 50,000 people, 6,000 cars, 180 coaches and 54,000 tonnes of freight every day.

Although the Channel Tunnel has been described as an incredible engineering feat, the cross-Channel link has endured its fair share of setbacks. During
25 construction, ten workers lost their lives, and to date, five fires have occurred inside the tunnel, leading on occasion to closures and travel disruption.

Answer these questions about the text that you've just read.
Circle the letter that matches the correct answer.

1. What was the Franco-British Channel Tunnel Treaty?

   A Permission for a tunnel to be built between France and England

   B The initial proposal for a tunnel across the Channel

   C A document declaring the Channel Tunnel officially open

   D The paperwork signed by President Franco and Edward Heath

2. Where along the tunnel did the breakthrough take place?

   A 15.7 miles from Coquelles

   B Closer to Kent than Calais

   C 31.4 miles from Folkestone

   D Closer to Calais than Kent

3. When was the Channel Tunnel officially opened?

   A 1996

   B 1988

   C 1994

   D 1990

4. According to the text, who was present at the tunnel's official opening ceremony?

   A Two tunnellers

   B A British sovereign

   C A French mining engineer

   D Georges Pompidou

5. According to the passage, which of the following must be false?

A The Channel Tunnel is not made up of just one tunnel.

B Tunnelling from England occurred at a faster rate than tunnelling from France

C A Channel Tunnel train departing at 10.35 am would arrive at circa. 11.10 am

D Since it opened, the tunnel has never had to close.

6. Which of the following is not mentioned in the passage?

A An access route built into the tunnel for urgent situations

B Which countries the flags held by Fagg and Phillippe represented

C The fatalities suffered during the tunnel's construction

D The photographs taken at the breakthrough

7. According to the passage, which of the following must be true?

A Albert Mathieu-Favier's plans for a Channel Tunnel were accepted.

B Channel Tunnel trains run seven days a week.

C All vehicles were permitted to travel on the Channel Tunnel straightaway.

D The Channel Tunnel is the most popular way to travel from France to Britain.

Find the word that means the same, or nearly the same, as the word on the left.

Example: **wide** flat straight <u>broad</u> long

8. **caution** obedience vigilance compulsion thoughtfulness

9. **wrongdoing** violence rebellion flaw misconduct

10. **vague** faded contorted indistinct concealed

11. **provoke** annoy concoct displease ignite

12. **changeable** irresponsible versatile volatile impartial

13. **kindness** endearment disposition esteem goodwill

Three of the words in each list are linked. Mark the word that is not related to these three.

Example: journal diary <u>textbook</u> notebook

14. educate learn teach coach

15. grate chop file slice

16. dissatisfy protest irritate anger

17. realist sceptic doubter cynic

18. douse submerge splash cleanse

19. berate reprimand scold torment

20. finesse exercise adeptness aptitude

END OF TEST

/20

Test 22

You have **10 minutes** to do this test. Work as quickly and accurately as you can.

Read this passage carefully and answer the questions that follow.

An extract from 'Anne of Green Gables'

"Good evening, Rachel," Marilla said briskly. "This is a real fine evening, isn't it? Won't you sit down? How are all your folks?"

Something that for lack of any other name might be called friendship existed and always had existed between Marilla Cuthbert and Mrs Rachel, in spite of — or
5 perhaps because of — their dissimilarity.

Marilla was a tall, thin woman, with angles and without curves; her dark hair showed some gray streaks and was always twisted up in a hard little knot behind with two wire hairpins stuck aggressively through it. She looked like a woman of narrow experience and rigid conscience, which she was; but there was a saving
10 something about her mouth which, if it had been ever so slightly developed, might have been considered indicative of a sense of humor.

"We're all pretty well," said Mrs Rachel. "I was kind of afraid YOU weren't, though, when I saw Matthew starting off today. I thought maybe he was going to the doctor's."

15 Marilla's lips twitched understandingly. She had expected Mrs Rachel up; she had known that the sight of Matthew jaunting off so unaccountably would be too much for her neighbour's curiosity.

"Oh, no, I'm quite well although I had a bad headache yesterday," she said. "Matthew went to Bright River. We're getting a little boy from an orphan asylum in
20 Nova Scotia and he's coming on the train tonight."

If Marilla had said that Matthew had gone to Bright River to meet a kangaroo from Australia Mrs Rachel could not have been more astonished. She was actually stricken dumb for five seconds. It was unsupposable that Marilla was making fun of her, but Mrs Rachel was almost forced to suppose it.

Lucy Maud Montgomery

Answer these questions about the text that you've just read.
Circle the letter that matches the correct answer.

1. Which of the following best describes Rachel and Marilla?

A They treat each other with disdain.

B They are more like acquaintances than friends.

C They distrust one another.

D They are both secretive.

2. What does the phrase "narrow experience and rigid conscience" (line 9) tell us about Marilla's personality?

A She is inept and flighty.

B She is spiteful and forthright.

C She is naive and virtuous.

D She is uneducated and anxious.

3. According to the text, which of the following is Marilla's one redeeming feature?

A Her mouth

B Her height

C Her figure

D Her hair

4. "Marilla's lips twitched understandingly" (line 15).
What is it that Marilla understands?

A Why Rachel might have thought she was ill

B That inquisitiveness has got the better of Rachel

C That Rachel's curiosity has been abated

D Where Matthew went to

5. What do you think is the purpose of Rachel's visit?

A She was concerned about Marilla being ill.

B She was concerned about Matthew being ill.

C She wanted to know where Matthew was going.

D She wanted to talk to Marilla about the boy she was adopting.

6. Why had Matthew gone to Bright River?

A To catch a train

B To travel onwards to Nova Scotia

C To visit a children's home

D To collect an orphan

7. Why is Rachel "stricken dumb" (line 23)?

A Marilla has never discussed adopting a child with her before.

B Rachel cannot believe that anyone would want to adopt a child.

C She doesn't want to believe that Marilla has adopted a child.

D She thinks Marilla is lying to her.

In each question below, the words can be rearranged to form a sentence. One word doesn't fit in the sentence. Underline the word that doesn't fit.

Example: red the has <u>ride</u> girl bicycle a

8. were snowman children at winked that convinced the the had

9. December for month said a manufacturers successful toy was

10. best across summer by relaxing are beach the holidays spent

11. lightning whole the bolts sky the of it of night illuminated

12. when a lips tea slurping Lisa her she sips sound makes

13. cycling usually swimming up and a make are running triathlon

14. decided hill high looked is the was up too and James

Mark the word outside the brackets that has a similar meaning to the words in both sets of brackets.

Example: (twig branch) (fasten attach) glue stick affix bough

15. (leap spring) (chamber cellar) jump basement vault store

16. (scheme plan) (extend protrude) venture project lengthen idea

17. (type kind) (mark burn) sort stamp variety brand

18. (begin commence) (jerk flinch) start twitch initiate jump

19. (consent permission) (penalty deterrent) approval fine sanction forfeit

20. (equal fellow) (squint stare) spy peer watch friend

END OF TEST

/20

Test 23

You have **10 minutes** to do this test. Work as quickly and accurately as you can.

Choose the correct words to complete the passage below.

School dinners versus packed lunches: the debate
1. enlivens / continues / promotes / encourages
. No one knows for sure which option is
2. nutritionally / nourished / healthier / wholesomeness
, but new findings indicate that the
3. firstly / previous / former / original
are outshining the latter in the quest to provide pupils with nutritious meals.
4. For / By / On / As
example, lower levels of fat and sugar are found in pupils who
5. eaten / has eaten / will eat / eat
school dinners compared to pupils who dine
6. indoors / inside / at home / homely
or who bring lunch with them to school.
7. Therefore / Despite / Contrary / However
, researchers believe that school meals

can still be improved, since lower levels of folate (a type 8. ☐ to ☐ of ☐ with ☐ on vitamin) were

9. ☐ screened ☐ prevailed ☐ contested ☐ detected in pupils frequenting the school canteen. One way to 10. ☐ surmount ☐ prolong ☐ increase ☐ exasperate

the amount of folate, suggested 11. ☐ by ☐ from ☐ under ☐ amidst researchers, is to 12. ☐ incorporating ☐ utilise ☐ included ☐ addition more

fresh ingredients in school meals.

Find the word that means the opposite, or nearly the opposite, of the word on the left.

Example: **first** later <u>last</u> next beginning

13. **lifeless** attractive lively transfixed eloquent

14. **far-fetched** reliable accurate plausible fundamental

15. **lenient** austere intense debatable bombastic

16. **hazy** insecure definitely clear sunshine

Mark the word outside the brackets that has a similar meaning to the words in both sets of brackets.

Example: (twig branch) (fasten attach) glue <u>stick</u> affix bough

17. (tight taut) (anxious nervous) worried rigid tense fretful
18. (field arena) (throw toss) pitch launch grounds fling
19. (complete conclude) (fasten close) affix seal finish attach
20. (cultivated cultured) (purified filtered) civilised treated courtly refined
21. (principle standard) (worth cost) moral sum price value

Complete the word on the right so that it means the same, or nearly the same, as the word on the left.

Example: scared [a][f][r][a][i][d]

22. fringe [p][ ][r][ ][p][h][ ][ ][y]
23. delicious [d][ ][l][ ][c][ ][ ][b][l][e]
24. sailor [m][ ][r][ ][n][ ][ ]
25. obstruct [i][ ][ ][e][ ][e]
26. steal [p][i][ ][f][e][ ]

END OF TEST

/ 26

Test 24

You have **10 minutes** to do this test. Work as quickly and accurately as you can.

Fill in the missing letters to complete the words in the following passage.

With a wealth of life experience and a good story to tell, a keen writer might

1. put pen to paper and c h r o n _ _ l _ their time on Earth
2. in what are commonly _ e f e _ r _ d to as *memoirs*. The term

memoirs comes from the French word *mémoire*, which means memory.

3. A person's memoirs form a c _ l l _ c t _ _ n of memories that
4. can s _ r e _ c _ as far back as their early
5. c _ i _ d _ o o _. Writing about yourself sounds like a fairly easy
6. task, but experts warn that it can be an emotional _ _ _ r n _ y of
7. self-discovery. The _ u _ _ _ r may have to face some testing questions,
8. such as what to i _ _ _ u d _ and whether to be
9. e _ t _ _ _ l y truthful or not. They could find themselves
10. _ e c a l _ _ n g a difficult period in their life which leaves them
11. drained and _ x h _ u _ t _ d by the time they have completed

just a few pages. Nonetheless, many consider memoir writing to be a

12. _ h e r _ p _ u _ i c and beneficial experience.

Find the word that means the same, or nearly the same, as the word on the left.

Example: **wide** flat straight <u>broad</u> long

13. **markedly** assumedly apparently determinately discernibly
14. **repeat** stutter recall reiterate restart
15. **disagreement** quarrel grumbling rejection defiance
16. **association** ally corporation workplace competitor
17. **temptation** provocation bullying enticement hatred

Three of the words in each list are linked. Mark the word that is not related to these three.

Example: journal diary <u>textbook</u> notebook

18. prompt trigger dissuade provoke
19. slide rotate revolve spin
20. emotional shy retiring reserved
21. enlarge dwindle broaden swell
22. control restrain curb halt

In each question below, the words can be rearranged to form a sentence. One word doesn't fit in the sentence. Underline the word that doesn't fit.

Example: red the has <u>ride</u> girl bicycle a

23. buy to deciding of tricky what can is kind computer

24. thinks interpreted can people that believe be dreams some

25. the torment cat you'll might it or don't regret neighbour's

26. to and in TV black white be only used were available programmes

END OF TEST

/ 26

Test 25

You have **10 minutes** to do this test. Work as quickly and accurately as you can.

Choose the correct words to complete the passage below.

Most bouncy castles are
1. ☐ leased ☐ let ☐ loaned ☐ hired
by customers to celebrate a
2. ☐ specially ☐ specialised ☐ special ☐ spacial
occasion. However, in August 2013, a bouncy castle was
3. ☐ employed ☐ put ☐ used ☐ rented
to a slightly different use; eight bouncers in Rugby, Warwickshire set
4. ☐ about ☐ on ☐ at ☐ in
beating the
5. ☐ existed ☐ establishing ☐ existing ☐ establish
world record for the
6. ☐ longer ☐ lengthier ☐ more long ☐ longest
team marathon on a bouncy castle. But this isn't the only world record that
7. ☐ has involved ☐ involving ☐ is involved ☐ had involved
a large inflatable. An unusual activity, which goes
8. ☐ across ☐ by ☐ in ☐ under
the name of *blobbing*, has also entered the

record books. Blobbing takes place on the water. An inflatable is

9. ☐ impartial
☐ partially
☐ completed
☐ filled

inflated; Participant A sits on one end, and Participant B jumps from a height onto the

10. ☐ exterior
☐ internal
☐ underneath
☐ opposite

side. Participant A is

11. ☐ subsequent
☐ since
☐ after
☐ then

fired into the air and lands in

the water. A blobbing world record was set in 2012

12. ☐ when
☐ by
☐ through
☐ from

a German blob team

reached a height of 22 metres.

Three of the words in each list are linked. Mark the word that is not related to these three.

Example: journal diary textbook notebook

13. scholar lecturer tutor instructor

14. cunning foolish trait sensible

15. haphazard random indiscriminate premeditated

16. subterranean underground celestial buried

17. nurse recover operate medicate

In each question below, the words can be rearranged to form a sentence. One word doesn't fit in the sentence. Underline the word that doesn't fit.

Example: red the has <u>ride</u> girl bicycle a

18. is launch perfect weather a kite flying windy for

19. Jade find shock astounded the cattery was in dogs to

20. borrowed may library at seven for days books up be to

21. marking handwriting difficult scruffy work grade makes deciphering

Mark the word outside the brackets that has a similar meaning to the words in both sets of brackets.

Example: (twig branch) (fasten attach) glue <u>stick</u> affix bough

22. (gather congregate) (construct build) meet assemble crowd erect

23. (general rough) (wide big) thick vague large broad

24. (bristly scratchy) (rude vulgar) coarse crass offensive uncivil

25. (decrease dwindle) (refuse reject) rebuff spurn decline lessen

26. (haughty arrogant) (tall high) grand imposing giant lofty

END OF TEST

/ 26

Puzzles 5

Time for a break! These puzzles are a great way to practise your **word making** skills.

Synonym Snake

Fill in the Synonym Snake with a synonym for each word below. Each synonym starts with the last letter of the previous synonym. The first and last letters of each word are given in the grey boxes.

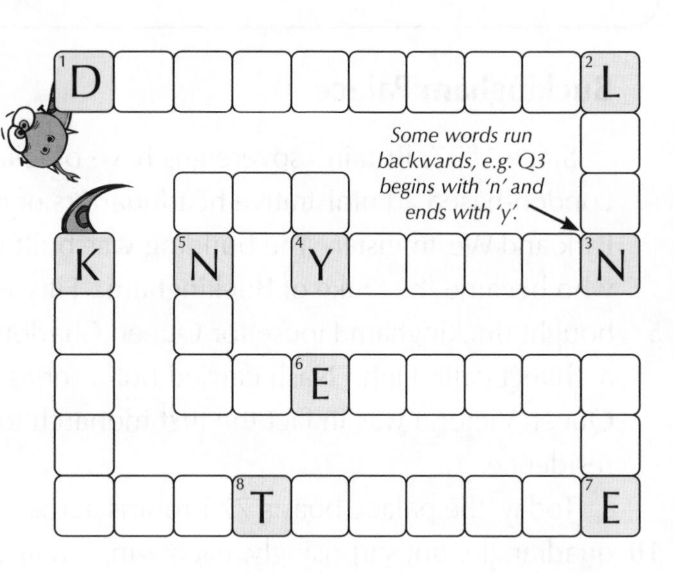

1. lovely
2. slim
3. inform
4. crave
5. innocent
6. guess
7. obvious
8. cooperation

What Letter am I?

a. If you take me out of a bridge, you'll find me at a wedding.

What letter am I? ____________

b. If you take me out of a marker, you'll find a creator.

What letter am I? ____________

c. If you take me out of a duvet, you'll find a song.

What letter am I? ____________

d. If you take me out of a planet, you'll find a shrub.

What letter am I? ____________

e. If you take me out of whisky, you'll find a mixer.

What letter am I? ____________

Test 26

You have **10 minutes** to do this test. Work as quickly and accurately as you can.

Read this passage carefully and answer the questions that follow.

Buckingham Palace

Since 1837, Britain's sovereigns have officially resided in Buckingham Palace, the London-based administrative headquarters of the monarch, which adjoins St James's Park and Westminster. The building was built in 1703 for John Sheffield, a politician who became the Duke of Buckingham. Fifty-eight years later, King George III
5 bought Buckingham House for Queen Charlotte, his spouse. In the 1820s, an architect called John Nash carried out a series of extensions for King George IV, but Queen Victoria was in fact the first monarch to make Buckingham Palace her official residence.

Today, the palace boasts 775 rooms across four wings which encompass a
10 quadrangle; not surprisingly, each wing's name includes a compass point in its title. Facing the gardens and to the west of the Grand Entrance are the chambers most often frequented by the Queen and members of the Royal Family. Collectively, these rooms are known as the State Rooms. The most southerly State Room is the Ball Room, which the West Gallery connects to the first of four rooms which afford
15 a view of the gardens; the State Dining Room often hosts large lunch parties, and many prominent figures have dined in this grandiose setting.

Each year, the Queen invites more than 50 000 guests to the palace, and in August and September, hundreds of thousands of visitors are willing to pay to pass through the palace's doors. The more frugal tourist, however, might be content
20 with simply admiring the façade and witnessing Changing the Guard which takes place on the palace's forecourt. During this ceremony, the privilege of guarding the sovereign is passed from one regiment to another. From 1st April to 31st July, this happens daily at 11.30 am. For all other months, Changing the Guard occurs at the same time, but on alternate days.

25 One royal tradition that occurs on a more ad hoc basis is the raising and lowering of the Royal Standard. A flag always flies above Buckingham Palace, but if the Queen is in residence, a Union Jack is replaced by the Royal Standard. It falls to the responsibility of the Flag Sergeant to ensure the correct flag is flying.

Answer these questions about the text that you've just read.
Circle the letter that matches the correct answer.

1. When did Queen Victoria take up residence in Buckingham Palace?

A In the 1820s

B In 1703

C In 1837

D In 1791

2. According to the text, which statement below applies to Buckingham Palace?

A It was made larger by King George III in the 1820s.

B It has wings on four sides which enclose a courtyard.

C It is a tourist hot-spot located to the east of St James's Park.

D It is not admired for its attractive appearance.

3. Where is the State Dining Room located?

A North of the Ball Room

B East of the Grand Entrance

C Inside the State Room

D Facing St James's Park

4. What do the palace's façade and Changing the Guard have in common?

A They are always present for tourists to see.

B They aim to protect the Queen.

C There is no charge to view them.

D They were designed to entertain tourists on a budget.

5. According to the text, which of the following is not true?

A The State Dining Room can accommodate 50,000 people.

B Buckingham Palace became larger in the 1820s.

C The gardens are opposite the State Rooms.

D Queen Charlotte was the first Queen to live in Buckingham Palace.

6. Which of the following is not mentioned in the text?

A A former name for Buckingham Palace

B The rooms where the Queen is most likely to be found

C Who is responsible for protecting the Queen

D The name of King George IV's wife

7. According to the text, which of the following must be true?

A Each wing has roughly 194 rooms.

B The Queen is not always in residence at Buckingham Palace.

C Queen Victoria was the next in line to the throne after King George IV.

D Changing the Guard will take place on 3rd August.

Complete the word on the right so that it means the same, or nearly the same, as the word on the left.

Example: scared [a][f][r][a][i][d]

8. stain [t][ ][r][ ][ ][ ][h]

9. enrage [i][ ][f][u][ ][ ][ ][t][e]

10. method [p][ ][ ][c][e][ ][ ]

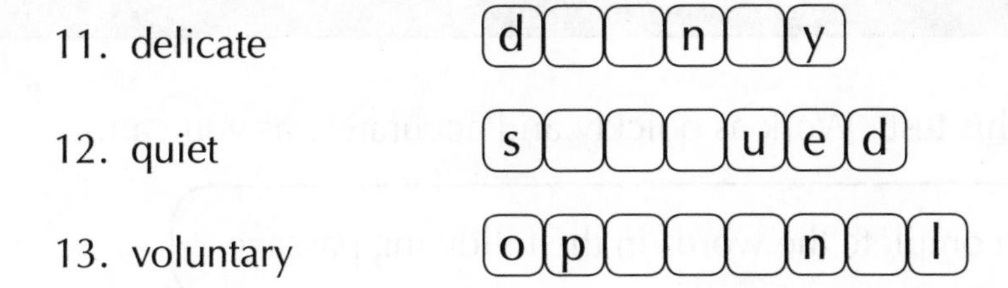

11. delicate — d _ _ n _ y

12. quiet — s _ _ _ u e d

13. voluntary — o p _ _ _ n _ l

Find the word that means the opposite, or nearly the opposite, of the word on the left.

Example: **first** later <u>last</u> next beginning

14. **accepted** tempestuous contentious reject disliked

15. **capable** heedless inept irrelevant absurd

16. **relax** toil increase activate incite

17. **participate** disengage proffer abstain disregard

18. **unknown** listed obtainable accustomed identified

19. **allow** illegitimate prohibit halted contrary

20. **success** mediocrity misdemeanour fail debacle

END OF TEST

/20

Test 27

You have **10 minutes** to do this test. Work as quickly and accurately as you can.

Fill in the missing letters to complete the words in the following passage.

1. If someone acts naughtily or mischievously, their b _ h a v _ _ _ r
2. could be described as *tomfoolery*, a term which is t _ o _ _ _ t
   to have come from a name that was often given to court jesters: Tom Fool.
3. One famous Tom Fool (who is r _ m _ _ r _ d to have been the
4. inspiration behind a c _ _ r a c _ e _ in one of Shakespeare's
   plays) was Thomas Skelton. Skelton was a court jester at Muncaster Castle,
5. Cumbria, during the sixteenth c _ n _ u _ _. According to legend,
6. Skelton is said to have directed _ i s _ t _ _ s who he disliked
7. towards the _ a n _ _ r o _ s quicksands along the River Esk.
8. It is also _ l _ e _ _ d that Skelton was responsible for the murder of
9. a local carpenter. When Skelton l _ _ r n _ d that his master's
10. daughter was in a relationship with the carpenter, he i n _ _ _ m _ d
11. his master immediately. Skelton then r _ c _ _ _ e d orders
12. to kill the carpenter, and so he c _ o p _ _ d off the poor man's head.

Mark the word outside the brackets that has a similar meaning to the words in both sets of brackets.

Example: (twig branch) (fasten attach) glue stick affix bough

13. (chatter prattle) (walk hike) talk wander babble ramble
14. (scratch notch) (result outcome) total nick score sum
15. (determination decision) (settle rectify) reconcile resolve idea clarify
16. (situation circumstance) (box receptacle) position status case basket
17. (responsible accountable) (likely inclined) liable prone guilty apt

Three of the words in each list are linked. Mark the word that is not related to these three.

Example: journal diary textbook notebook

18. scowl smile frown laugh
19. nest set hollow sty
20. twilight moonlight midnight dusk
21. pitfalls spoils catches snags
22. conceal divulge disclose confess

Find the word that means the same, or nearly the same, as the word on the left.

Example: **wide** flat straight broad long

23. **fascinated** emotional riveted aroused curious
24. **postpone** prolong interrupt reappoint adjourn
25. **attempt** endeavour trial investigation ambition
26. **downcast** passive subdued inanimate distant

END OF TEST

/26

Test 28

You have **10 minutes** to do this test. Work as quickly and accurately as you can.

Choose the correct words to complete the passage below.

Over the years, many independent polls have been
1. ☐ conducted ☐ run ☐ completed ☐ carried
out to establish which biscuit is the most
2. ☐ favourite ☐ popular ☐ dearest ☐ best-loved
in the UK. Although results sometimes
3. ☐ vary ☐ range ☐ alter ☐ divide
, one biscuit in particular is
4. ☐ reliable ☐ guaranteed ☐ always ☐ undoubted
a strong contender: the chocolate digestive. Digestives were first
5. ☐ advised ☐ inventive ☐ intended ☐ developed
in 1839 to
6. ☐ aided ☐ aid ☐ aiding ☐ had aided
digestion, and currently
7. ☐ their ☐ there ☐ they're ☐ them
ingredients include brown wheat flour, sugar, malt extract, vegetable oil, raising agents and salt. Chocolate was applied to one side
8. ☐ in ☐ at ☐ of ☐ for

digestives some years later, 9. ☐ providing ☐ enabling ☐ allowing ☐ giving the consumer with the choice of a milk or

dark chocolate biscuit. Some more novel 10. ☐ type ☐ kind ☐ assortment ☐ varieties have also featured hints of

orange or mint in the chocolate mix, and biscuit lovers 11. ☐ of ☐ with ☐ for ☐ in an extra sweet tooth

might be pleased to hear 12. ☐ about ☐ that ☐ which ☐ since some digestives also include a layer of caramel.

Complete the word on the right so that it means the opposite, or nearly the opposite, of the word on the left.

Example: heavy [l][i][g][h][t]

13. free [ ][ ][p][ ][i][ ][e]

14. cowardice [ ][r][ ][v][ ][r][ ][ ]

15. hurry [ ][a][ ][d][ ][e]

16. former [l][ ][t][ ][ ][r]

Mark the word outside the brackets that has a similar meaning to the words in both sets of brackets.

Example: (twig branch) (fasten attach) glue <u>stick</u> affix bough

17. (clothe attire) (decorate adorn) embellish wear beautify dress

18. (baffle confuse) (game riddle) puzzle bemuse toy problem

19. (deliberate intentional) (aware awake) intended alive conscious meant

20. (acceptable average) (sensible rational) reasonable adequate wise valid

21. (expand on add to) (detailed intricate) increase elaborate full exact

Three of the words in each list are linked. Mark the word that is not related to these three.

Example: journal diary <u>textbook</u> notebook

22. program mouse screen keyboard

23. flawless spotless gleaming pristine

24. poignant moving touching sympathetic

25. insensitive callous manipulative heartless

26. anecdotal curative healing restorative

END OF TEST

/26

Test 29

You have **10 minutes** to do this test. Work as quickly and accurately as you can.

Read this passage carefully and answer the questions that follow.

An Extract from 'The Raven'

Once upon a midnight dreary, while I pondered, weak and weary,
Over many a quaint and curious volume of forgotten lore*,
While I nodded, nearly napping, suddenly there came a tapping,
As of some one gently rapping, rapping at my chamber door.
5 "'T is some visitor," I muttered, "tapping at my chamber door—
Only this, and nothing more."

Ah, distinctly I remember it was in the bleak December,
And each separate dying ember wrought its ghost upon the floor.
Eagerly I wished the morrow;—vainly I had sought to borrow
10 From my books surcease** of sorrow—sorrow for the lost Lenore—
For the rare and radiant maiden whom the angels name Lenore—
Nameless here for evermore.

And the silken sad uncertain rustling of each purple curtain
Thrilled me—filled me with fantastic terrors never felt before;
15 So that now, to still the beating of my heart, I stood repeating
"'T is some visitor entreating entrance at my chamber door—
Some late visitor entreating entrance at my chamber door;—
This it is, and nothing more."

Presently my soul grew stronger; hesitating then no longer,
20 "Sir," said I, "or Madam, truly your forgiveness I implore;
But the fact is I was napping, and so gently you came rapping,
And so faintly you came tapping, tapping at my chamber door,
That I scarce was sure I heard you"—here I opened wide the door;—
Darkness there, and nothing more.

* lore — *stories*
** surcease — *relief*

Edgar Allan Poe

Answer these questions about the text that you've just read.
Circle the letter that matches the correct answer.

1. Where is the narrator when he hears a tapping noise?

A In a library

B In a graveyard

C In his bedroom

D In a church

2. What is happening to the fire?

A It is going out.

B It is being blown by a breeze.

C It is spreading across the floor.

D It is burning brightly.

3. What is the narrator doing to try and stop feeling sad?

A He is closing the curtains.

B He is thinking of Lenore.

C He is reading something.

D He is stoking the fire.

4. "whom the angels name Lenore— / Nameless here for evermore." (lines 11-12).
What do these lines tell you about Lenore?

A She has moved away.

B She is an angel.

C She has disappeared.

D She is dead.

5. Why does the narrator repeat himself in lines 16 and 17?

A To cure his heartache

B To convince himself that there is nothing to fear

C To make himself understood

D To warn the visitor that the room is occupied

6. Which two of the following are reasons why the narrator does not answer the door immediately?

1) He is frightened.
2) He doesn't want to get out of bed.
3) He doesn't want any visitors.
4) He is half asleep when he hears the noise.

A 1 and 2

B 1 and 4

C 2 and 3

D 2 and 4

7. Why does the narrator finally address the visitor?

A Because he is lonely

B Because he knows who it is

C Because he needs cheering up

D Because he feels more confident

Three of the words in each list are linked. Mark the word that is not related to these three.

Example: journal diary <u>textbook</u> notebook

8. leg arm hand figure
9. dormitory auditorium canteen study
10. support encouragement attention approval
11. reprieve pardon amnesty sanction
12. snack supper brunch dinner
13. treasured priceless nominal valuable
14. examine analyse study criticise

Mark the word outside the brackets that has a similar meaning to the words in both sets of brackets.

Example: (twig branch) (fasten attach) glue <u>stick</u> affix bough

15. (redness spots) (reckless impulsive) hasty rash blemish hurried
16. (possession belonging) (quality attribute) property goods trait hallmark
17. (replicate duplicate) (restate reiterate) rehearse recap repeat reword
18. (conference meeting) (custom practice) convention forum habit show
19. (upland heath) (berth dock) secure field port moor
20. (thoroughly completely) (admirably ably) wholly well carefully warmly

END OF TEST

/20

Test 30

You have **10 minutes** to do this test. Work as quickly and accurately as you can.

Fill in the missing letters to complete the words in the following passage.

1. Situated along the west c _ _ _ t of North America, in the American state
2. of California, lies the second most _ e _ s _ l y populated city in the
3. United States. _ r _ _ n _ eight million people live in San Francisco,
4. and a f _ r _ h _ _ seventeen million tourists visit the city each year.
5. With its _ a m _ _ s attractions, retro cable cars, and shops galore, the
6. city never disappoints. Take, for e _ _ _ p _ e, the Golden Gate
7. Bridge. Arguably the most i c _ n _ _ landmark in San Francisco, it
8. stretches 1.7 miles across the channel b _ t _ _ _ n San Francisco Bay
9. and the Pacific O _ _ a _. A short drive south-east of the bridge takes you
   to the San Francisco Museum of Modern Art, which brings in over 600,000 visitors
10. every _ _ _ r. But tourists don't just visit the urban areas of San Francisco;
11. its beaches are widely popular _ m _ _ g _ t surfers, and its many
12. parks _ t _ r a _ t high levels of tourism.

Three of the words in each list are linked. Mark the word that is not related to these three.

Example: journal diary textbook notebook

13. brook pond stream river

14. watchtower prison cell dungeon

15. strew disperse scatter muster

16. char toast scorch singe

17. problematic puzzling investigative mystifying

Mark the word outside the brackets that has a similar meaning to the words in both sets of brackets.

Example: (twig branch) (fasten attach) glue stick affix bough

18. (bottom plinth) (camp headquarters) base ground post foundation

19. (instruct teach) (procession line) convoy train coach queue

20. (provide award) (elasticity flexibility) give present stretch bestow

21. (prefer approve) (kindness courtesy) endorse favour gesture will

22. (coercion duress) (power strength) violence might energy force

Complete the word on the right so that it means the opposite, or nearly the opposite, of the word on the left.

Example: heavy [l][i][g][h][t]

23. compliment [i][ ][s][ ][ ][ ]

24. illusion [ ][ ][a][ ][i][ ][y]

25. confront [e][ ][ ][d][ ]

26. clumsy [d][e][ ][t][e][ ][ ][ ][s]

END OF TEST

/ 26

Test 31

You have **10 minutes** to do this test. Work as quickly and accurately as you can.

Read this passage carefully and answer the questions that follow.

The Telephone

The invention of the telephone is often credited to Alexander Graham Bell, who acquired a patent for his communications device in 1876. The 19th century, however, saw many scientists experiment with electrical communication. Therefore, identifying a definitive inventor of the telephone is no easy feat.

5 Fifteen years before Bell patented his telephone, a German scientist presented the 'Reis telephone'. Inspired by a similar design to that suggested by engineer Charles Bourseul seven years earlier, Johann Philipp Reis used his invention to transmit the phrase "The horse does not eat cucumber salad" over a distance of 100 metres. He chose this phrase because it is difficult to understand in German, and it would serve as
10 proof that the device worked if the speech could be heard clearly. He also introduced the term "telephon" to describe his invention. However, in 1862, Reis's invention was rejected by other scientists, as it was thought to be an unrealistic concept.

Between 1856 and 1870, it is claimed that inventor Antonio Meucci developed over 30 different telephone-like prototypes. He used his inventions to communicate
15 with his wife — who was often in bed due to illness — while he was in his basement laboratory. Unfortunately, Meucci was unable to finance his invention further or acquire the necessary patent to legally claim the idea as his own. It is thought by some that had he been able to carry on his work, he would have become widely acknowledged as the inventor of the telephone.

20 Many scientists therefore seemed to have been on the cusp of claiming credit for the invention of the telephone. However, some argue that the strongest contender for this praise (bar Bell, that is) was Bell's fellow engineer Elisha Gray, who developed a telephone prototype in the same year that Bell acquired his patent. The question of whether one inventor copied the other is still debated to this day.

Answer these questions about the text that you've just read.
Circle the letter that matches the correct answer.

1. Why are people uncertain about who invented the telephone?

A Because people kept their inventions secret

B Because numerous telephone prototypes existed

C Because more than one person was present at each experiment

D Because patents were expensive during the 19th century

2. When did Bourseul put forward his design for a telephone?

A In 1869

B In 1861

C In 1854

D In 1856

3. Which of the following explains why Reis said "The horse does not eat cucumber salad" over his telephone?

A This sentence put the sound quality of his telephone to the test.

B This sentence is a famous tongue twister in Germany.

C This sentence was precisely long enough for Reis's voice to be heard 100 metres away.

D This sentence is the hardest to pronounce in German.

4. According to the passage, which of the following must be true?

A The three years Reis spent on his device were to no avail.

B Reis invented the word 'telephone'.

C The first person Meucci telephoned was his wife.

D Alexander Bell was an engineer.

5. Why did Meucci not become the inventor of the telephone?

A His wife was ill.

B He was unable to officially register himself as the creator of the invention.

C He focused his attention on trying to communicate over too short a distance.

D Financing over 30 prototypes became impossible to sustain.

6. According to the passage, which of the following must be false?

A Gray produced a prototype for his telephone in 1876.

B Gray was working alongside Bell when Bell patented his telephone.

C It was pure coincidence that Bell acquired a patent around the time that Gray developed his idea.

D Today, more than one scientist is on the verge of being identified as the inventor of the telephone.

7. Which of the following is not mentioned in the text?

A How challenging it is to state who invented the telephone

B Who dismissed Reis's invention

C What use Meucci's prototypes served

D Where Reis developed his telephone

Find the word that means the opposite, or nearly the opposite, of the word on the left.

Example: **first** later <u>last</u> next beginning

8. **slow** prompt hastily hurry concise
9. **sociable** untalkative solitude serene reclusive
10. **celebrate** mourn endure abide scold
11. **disappear** produce recover present materialise
12. **intensify** subside defocus distract discredit
13. **modesty** courage confidence egotism charm

In each question below, the words can be rearranged to form a sentence. One word doesn't fit in the sentence. Underline the word that doesn't fit.

Example: red the has <u>ride</u> girl bicycle a

14. mistakes your it work submit in then check for hand
15. never bad pocket a interest saving thing is money your
16. a time the have pretended at good party Louise was to
17. for shoppers inconvenience were caused any awarded vouchers off
18. can sense puzzle achievement give a of you a solving able
19. be cold tonight ought it enough snow should to
20. football going field after am play I to school

END OF TEST

/20

Test 32

You have **10 minutes** to do this test. Work as quickly and accurately as you can.

Choose the correct words to complete the passage below.

Rolling a piece of cheese down a hill and chasing [1. ☐ along ☐ to ☐ after ☐ before] it in an attempt to become cheese-rolling champion isn't what most people would [2. ☐ think ☐ contemplate ☐ consider ☐ see] a normal activity. [3. ☐ Despite ☐ Contrary ☐ However ☐ On the other hand], this is precisely what [4. ☐ appears ☐ happens ☐ occurrence ☐ results] at the annual cheese-rolling festival [5. ☐ who ☐ where ☐ when ☐ which] takes place in Gloucestershire. Every year, towards the end of May, an unofficial event takes place where a round [6. ☐ peace ☐ proportion ☐ piece ☐ fraction] of Double Gloucester, weighing 9 lb, is set rolling down Cooper's Hill [7. ☐ but ☐ yet ☐ for ☐ with] competitors to chase after. The winner is the first runner to cross

8. ☐ a
☐ an
☐ this
☐ the

finish line.

9. ☐ Before
☐ After
☐ When
☐ Although

everyone

10. ☐ aiming
☐ aimed
☐ aims
☐ had aimed

to catch the cheese, this rarely happens, as it has

11. ☐ approximate
☐ estimated
☐ roughly
☐ roundly

a one second head start and can

12. ☐ reach
☐ exceeded
☐ accelerate
☐ adapt

speeds of up to 70 mph.

Mark the word outside the brackets that has a similar meaning to the words in both sets of brackets.

Example: (twig branch) (fasten attach) glue stick affix bough

13. (chest suitcase) (nose snout) beak coffer box trunk

14. (suffer tolerate) (last survive) undergo endure persist bear

15. (mixture combination) (matrimony wedlock) marriage wedding blend unit

16. (responsibility obligation) (tax tariff) rate duty task levy

17. (function operate) (labour exertion) perform toil work effort

Three of the words in each list are linked. Mark the word that is not related to these three.

Example: journal diary <u>textbook</u> notebook

18. nib ink fountain lid
19. track carriage engine seat
20. hazardous perilous dangerous peculiar
21. bleak dark bright light
22. auditory nasal armful optical

Find the word that means the same, or nearly the same, as the word on the left.

Example: **wide** flat straight <u>broad</u> long

23. **private** mysterious classified anonymous unspecified
24. **casual** spontaneous unofficial informal unprofessional
25. **spoil** dirt affect alter ruin
26. **descriptive** illustrative picturesque imagery complete

END OF TEST

/26

Puzzles 6

Time for a break! These puzzles are a great way to practise your **spelling** skills.

Repair It

Each of the words below has one spelling mistake. Circle the incorrect letter in each word, and write the correct letter into the numbered box. The correct letters give the answer to the joke!

1. disobediunt
This first one has been done for you!

2. telaport

3. sistem

4. relasion

5. dreeming

6. balence

What did the pirate say on his eighthieth birthday?

5 3 1 6 4 2

☐ ☐ e m ☐ ☐ ☐ y !

Cube Words

Using just the letters in the cube, can you spell the answers to the clues? You can only use each letter once in each word.

P	C	L
S	E	A
N	A	D

Every answer must use the letter 'E'.

a verb meaning 'move to music' ....

another word for 'location' ....

something you light with a match ....

something found on a fish ....

Can you find the nine letter word? _ _ _ _ _ _ _ _ _
Hint: it's another word for 'scenery'.

